WORKING PAPERS I

to accompany

WALGENBACH HANSON HAMRE

PRINCIPLES OF ACCOUNTING

FIFTH EDITION

WORKING PAPERS I
to accompany

WALGENBACH HANSON HAMRE

PRINCIPLES OF ACCOUNTING

FIFTH EDITION

Chapters 1–16

HBJ

Harcourt Brace Jovanovich, Publishers
San Diego New York Chicago Austin Washington, D.C.
London Sydney Tokyo Toronto

ISBN: 0-15-571397-3
Printed in the United States of America

TO THE STUDENT

These Working Papers are for use in solving the problems, alternate problems, business decision problems, and annual report problems in Chapters 1–16 of our *Principles of Accounting,* Fifth Edition. They are identified by problem number and company name, and they contain the headings, columns, and other necessary aids to assist you in organizing your answers and solutions. When appropriate, we have supplied problem data to save you time. **Forms with six or more columns, such as worksheets, cash receipts journals, cash disbursement journals, and registers, are on fold-out pages at the back of this volume.** Note that where parts of the working papers for a particular problem are printed out of order, as is sometimes necessary, or where solving the problem requires turning to a fold-out page, **cross-references are printed on the forms** to save you time.

Paul H. Walgenbach

Ernest I. Hanson

James C. Hamre

Name ______________________

Section ______________________

1-27

R. L. Harding Appraisal Service

(a) and (b)

	Assets							=	Liabilities	+	Owner's Equity
	Cash	+	Accounts Receivable	+	Supplies on Hand	+	Prepaid Rent	=	Accounts Payable	+	R. L. Harding, Capital
Balance											
Transactions											
(1)											
(2)											
(3)											
(4)											
(5)											
(6)											
(7)											
(8)											
(9)											
(10)											
(11)											

Name ____________________

Section ____________________

1-27

R. L. Harding Appraisal Service

R. L. Harding Appraisal Service
Income Statement
For the Month of January, 19XX

(c)

Revenue	
Expenses	

(d)

R. L. Harding Appraisal Service
Statement of Owner's Equity
For the Month of January, 19XX

Name

Section

1-28
Jackson Detective Agency

(a)

(b) (2) Borrowed $2,000, giving a note payable.

(3)

(4)

(5)

(6)

(7)

(8)

(9)

(10)

(c)

Name ____________________

Section ____________________

(a)

Arrow Delivery Service
Income Statement
For the Month of March, 19XX

Revenue

Expenses

(b)

Arrow Delivery Service
Statement of Owner's Equity
For the Month of March, 19XX

Name ____________________

Section ____________________

1-29
Arrow Delivery Service

Arrow Delivery Service
Balance Sheet
March 31, 19XX

(c)

Assets		Liabilities	
		Owner's Equity	

Name ______________________________

Section ______________________________

1-30
Brittany Catering Service

(a) and (b)

Brittany Catering Service
Balance Sheets

			May 31, 19XX	June 2, 19XX
		Assets		
		Liabilities		
		Stockholders' Equity		

Name ______________________________

Section ______________________________

1-31

Wilderness Fly-In Service, Inc.

(a) and (b)

	Assets				= Liabilities +	Stockholders' Equity	
	Cash +	Accounts Receivable +	Supplies on Hand +	Prepaid Insurance =	Accounts Payable +	Capital Stock +	Retained Earnings
Transactions							
(1)							
(2)							
(3)							
(4)							
(5)							
(6)							
(7)							
(8)							
(9)							
(10)							
(11)							
(12)							
(13)							

Name ______________________________

Section ______________________________

1-31

Wilderness Fly-In Service, Inc.

Wilderness Fly-In Service, Inc.
Income Statement
For the Month of June, 19XX

(c)

	Revenue			
	Expenses			

Name ______________________

Section ______________________

1-32
Whitney Packaging Service

(a)

Whitney Packaging Service
Balance Sheets

		December 31,	
		This Year	Last Year
Assets			
Liabilities			
Owner's Equity			
(b)			

Name ______________________

Section ______________________

1-27A

Stewart Answering Service

(a) and (b)

	Assets							=	Liabilities	+	Owner's Equity
	Cash	+	Accounts Receivable	+	Supplies on Hand	+	Prepaid Rent	=	Accounts Payable	+	E. Stewart, Capital
Balance											
Transactions											
(1)											
(2)											
(3)											
(4)											
(5)											
(6)											
(7)											
(8)											
(9)											
(10)											
(11)											

Name ______________________________

Section ______________________________

1-27A

Stewart Answering Service

Stewart Answering Service
Income Statement
For the Month of January, 19XX

(c)

Revenue

Expenses

(d)

Stewart Answering Service
Statement of Owner's Equity
For the Month of January, 19XX

Name ______________________

Section ______________________

1-28A

David Johnson, Consulting Engineer

(a)

(b) (2) Purchased supplies on account, $270.

(3)

(4)

(5)

(6)

(7)

(8)

(9)

(10)

(c)

Name ______________________

Section ______________________

1-29A

R. Jennings, Interior Decorator

(a)

R. Jennings, Interior Decorator
Income Statement
For the Year Ended December 31, 19XX

Revenue	
Expenses	

(b)

R. Jennings, Interior Decorator
Statement of Owner's Equity
For the Year Ended December 31, 19XX

Name ____________________

Section ____________________

(c)

R. Jennings, Interior Decorator
Balance Sheet
December 31, 19XX

Assets		Liabilities	
		Owner's Equity	

Name ____________________

Section ____________________

1-30A

Carr Plumbing Contractors, Inc.

(a) and (b)

Carr Plumbing Contractors, Inc.
Balance Sheets

	June 30, 19XX	July 2, 19XX
Assets		
Liabilities		
Stockholders' Equity		

Name ______________________

Section ______________________

1-31A
Psychological Resources

(a) and (b)

		Assets							=	Liabilities	+	Owner's Equity
	Cash	+	Accounts Receivable	+	Supplies on Hand	+	Prepaid Rent	=	Accounts Payable	+	J. Atwood, Capital
Transactions											
(1)											
(2)											
(3)											
(4)											
(5)											
(6)											
(7)											
(8)											
(9)											
(10)											
(11)											

Name ______________________

Section ______________________

1-31A
Psychological Resources

Psychological Resources
Income Statement
For the Month of June, 19XX

(c)

Revenue	
Expenses	

Curtis Janitorial Service, Inc.
Balance Sheets

(a)

Assets			
Liabilities			
Stockholders' Equity			
(b)			

Name ______________________

Section ______________________

Chapter 1

Business Decision Problem

Ideal Pest Control

Name ______________________

Section ______________________

2-23

James Cruz, Electrical Contractor

(a)

Cash

Accounts Receivable

Supplies on Hand

Prepaid Insurance

Equipment

Truck

Notes Payable

Accounts Payable

J. Cruz, Capital

J. Cruz, Drawing

Service Revenue

Rent Expense

Wages Expense

Utilities Expense

Truck Expense

Advertising Expense

Supplies Expense

Insurance Expense

Name ______________________

Section ______________________

James Cruz, Electrical Contractor
Trial Balance
May 31, 19XX

(b)

			Debit	Credit

Name ____________________

Section ____________________

(a)

Nolan's Waterproofing Service
Trial Balance
January 31, 19XX

			Debit	Credit

(b)

Nolan's Waterproofing Service
Income Statement
For the Month of January, 19XX

Revenue

Expenses

Name ____________________

Section ____________________

Nolan's Waterproofing Service
Balance Sheet
January 31, 19XX

(c)

Assets			*Liabilities*		
			Owner's Equity		

Name ______________________

Section ______________________

2-25

Cynthia Martin, Market Analyst

(a) (1) Cynthia Martin invested $20,000 of her personal funds in her business.

(2)

(3)

(4)

(5)

(6)

(7)

(8)

(9)

(b)

Name ____________________

Section ____________________

2-26
Artforms

(a)

Cash — Account No.

Date 19XX		Description	Post. Ref.	Debit*	Credit	Balance
July	1	Balance				11500

Accounts Receivable — Account No.

Date 19XX		Description	Post. Ref.	Debit*	Credit	Balance
July	1	Balance				16200

Prepaid Rent — Account No.

Date 19XX		Description	Post. Ref.	Debit*	Credit	Balance
July	1	Balance				1200

Name ______________________________

Section ______________________________

2-26
Artforms

(a) (*continued*)

Supplies on Hand — Account No.

Date 19XX		Description	Post. Ref.	Debit*	Credit	Balance
July	1	Balance				7400

Notes Payable — Account No.

Date 19XX		Description	Post. Ref.	Debit	Credit*	Balance
July	1	Balance				5000

Accounts Payable — Account No.

Date 19XX		Description	Post. Ref.	Debit	Credit*	Balance
July	1	Balance				1600

S. Chen, Capital — Account No.

Date 19XX		Description	Post. Ref.	Debit	Credit*	Balance
July	1	Balance				29700

Name ______________________________

Section ______________________________

(a) (*continued*)

S. Chen, Drawing — Account No.

Date 19XX		Description	Post. Ref.	Debit*	Credit	Balance

Service Fees Earned — Account No.

Date 19XX		Description	Post. Ref.	Debit	Credit*	Balance

Rent Expense — Account No.

Date 19XX		Description	Post. Ref.	Debit*	Credit	Balance

Salaries Expense — Account No.

Date 19XX		Description	Post. Ref.	Debit*	Credit	Balance

Name ____________________

Section ____________________

2-26
Artforms

(a) (continued)

Delivery Expense — Account No.

Date 19XX		Description	Post. Ref.	Debit*	Credit	Balance

Advertising Expense — Account No.

Date 19XX		Description	Post. Ref.	Debit	Credit	Balance

Utilities Expense — Account No.

Date 19XX		Description	Post. Ref.	Debit	Credit	Balance

Supplies Expense — Account No.

Date 19XX		Description	Post. Ref.	Debit	Credit	Balance

Name ______________________

Section ______________________

(b)

Artforms
Trial Balance
July 31, 19XX

			Debit	Credit

(c)

Artforms
Income Statement
For the Month of July, 19XX

Revenue

Expenses

Name ______________________

Section ______________________

2-26
Artforms

Artforms
Statement of Owner's Equity
For the Month of July, 19XX

(d)

Name ______________________

Section ______________________

(e)

Artforms
Balance Sheet
July 31, 19XX

Assets			*Liabilities*		
			Owner's Equity		

Name ____________________

Section ____________________

2-27

Wilderness Fly-In Service, Inc.

(a)

Cash Account No.

Date 19XX		Description	Post. Ref.	Debit*	Credit	Balance
Aug.	1	Balance				546 50

Accounts Receivable Account No.

Date 19XX		Description	Post. Ref.	Debit*	Credit	Balance
Aug.	1	Balance				315 00

Supplies on Hand Account No.

Date 19XX		Description	Post. Ref.	Debit*	Credit	Balance
Aug.	1	Balance				192 00

Name ____________________

Section ____________________

2-27

Wilderness Fly-In Service, Inc.

(a) *(continued)*

Prepaid Insurance

Account No.

Date 19XX		Description	Post. Ref.	Debit*	Credit	Balance
Aug.	1	Balance				4800

Notes Payable

Account No.

Date 19XX		Description	Post. Ref.	Debit	Credit*	Balance
Aug.	1	Balance				2500

Accounts Payable

Account No.

Date 19XX		Description	Post. Ref.	Debit	Credit*	Balance
Aug.	1	Balance				4200

Capital Stock

Account No.

Date 19XX		Description	Post. Ref.	Debit	Credit*	Balance
Aug.	1	Balance				80000

Name ____________________

Section ____________________

2-27

Wilderness Fly-In Service, Inc.

(a) (continued)

Retained Earnings — Account No.

Date 19XX		Description	Post. Ref.	Debit	Credit*	Balance
Aug.	1	Balance				23450

Service Fees Earned — Account No.

Date 19XX		Description	Post. Ref.	Debit	Credit*	Balance

Wages Expense — Account No.

Date 19XX		Description	Post. Ref.	Debit*	Credit	Balance

Advertising Expense — Account No.

Date 19XX		Description	Post. Ref.	Debit*	Credit	Balance

Name ______________________

Section ______________________

2-27

Wilderness Fly-In Service, Inc.

(a) (continued)

Rent Expense — Account No.

Date 19XX		Description	Post. Ref.	Debit*	Credit	Balance

Supplies Expense — Account No.

Date 19XX		Description	Post. Ref.	Debit*	Credit	Balance

Insurance Expense — Account No.

Date 19XX		Description	Post. Ref.	Debit*	Credit	Balance

Miscellaneous Expense — Account No.

Date 19XX		Description	Post. Ref.	Debit*	Credit	Balance

Name ____________________

Section ____________________

2-27

Wilderness Fly-In Service, Inc.

Wilderness Fly-In Service, Inc.
Trial Balance
August 31, 19XX

(b)

			Debit	Credit

(c)

Wilderness Fly-In Service, Inc.
Income Statement
For the Month of August, 19XX

	Revenue			
	Expenses			

Name ____________________

Section ____________________

Wilderness Fly-In Service, Inc.
Balance Sheet
August 31, 19XX

(d)

Assets		***Liabilities***	
		Stockholders' Equity	

Name ______________________

Section ______________________

2-28

Ross Janitorial Service

Ross Janitorial Service
Corrected Trial Balance
January 31, 19XX

			Debit	Credit

Name ____________________

Section ____________________

2-23A

Amy Tyson, Tax Accountant

(a)

Cash

Accounts Receivable

Office Supplies on Hand

Prepaid Insurance

Office Furniture and Fixtures

Notes Payable

Accounts Payable

A. Tyson, Capital

A. Tyson, Drawing

Professional Fees Earned

Rent Expense

Salaries Expense

Supplies Expense

Utilities Expense

Insurance Expense

Name ____________________

Section ____________________

2-23A

Amy Tyson, Tax Accountant

Amy Tyson, Tax Accountant
Trial Balance
June 30, 19XX

(b)

			Debit	Credit

Name ______________________

Section ______________________

2-24A

R. Dodd, Investment Counselor

(a)

R. Dodd, Investment Counselor
Trial Balance
January 31, 19XX

			Debit	Credit

(b)

R. Dodd, Investment Counselor
Income Statement
For the Month of January, 19XX

Revenue

Expenses

Name ____________________

Section ____________________

(c)

R. Dodd, Investment Counselor
Balance Sheet
January 31, 19XX

Assets		***Liabilities***	
		Owner's Equity	

Name ____________________

Section ____________________

2-25A

Daniel Kelly, Attorney

(a) (1) Daniel Kelly invested $17,000 of his personal funds in his law firm.

(2)

(3)

(4)

(5)

(6)

(7)

(8)

(9)

(10)

(11)

(b)

Name ______________________

Section ______________________

2-26A

Thorp Dance Studio

(a)

Cash

Account No.

Date 19XX		Description	Post. Ref.	Debit*	Credit	Balance
June	1	Balance				12600

Accounts Receivable

Account No.

Date 19XX		Description	Post. Ref.	Debit*	Credit	Balance
June	1	Balance				4350

Prepaid Insurance

Account No.

Date 19XX		Description	Post. Ref.	Debit*	Credit	Balance
June	1	Balance				720

Name ____________________

Section ____________________

2-26A

Thorp Dance Studio

(a) (*continued*)

Supplies on Hand

Account No.

Date 19XX		*Description*	*Post. Ref.*	*Debit**	*Credit*	*Balance*
June	1	Balance				650

Notes Payable

Account No.

Date 19XX		*Description*	*Post. Ref.*	*Debit*	*Credit**	*Balance*
June	1	Balance				3000

Accounts Payable

Account No.

Date 19XX		*Description*	*Post. Ref.*	*Debit*	*Credit**	*Balance*
June	1	Balance				450

J. Thorp, Capital

Account No.

Date 19XX		*Description*	*Post. Ref.*	*Debit*	*Credit**	*Balance*
June	1	Balance				14870

Name ______________________

Section ______________________

2-26A

Thorp Dance Studio

(a) ***(continued)***

J. Thorp, Drawing — **Account No.**

Date 19XX		Description	Post. Ref.	Debit*	Credit	Balance

Instructional Fees Earned — **Account No.**

Date 19XX		Description	Post. Ref.	Debit	Credit*	Balance

Performance Revenue — **Account No.**

Date 19XX		Description	Post. Ref.	Debit	Credit*	Balance

Rent Expense — **Account No.**

Date 19XX		Description	Post. Ref.	Debit*	Credit	Balance

Name ______________________

Section ______________________

2-26A

Thorp Dance Studio

(a) *(continued)*

Supplies Expense — Account No.

Date 19XX		Description	Post. Ref.	Debit*	Credit	Balance

Insurance Expense — Account No.

Date 19XX		Description	Post. Ref.	Debit*	Credit	Balance

Utilities Expense — Account No.

Date 19XX		Description	Post. Ref.	Debit*	Credit	Balance

Advertising Expense — Account No.

Date 19XX		Description	Post. Ref.	Debit*	Credit	Balance

Name ______________________

Section ______________________

2-26A

Thorp Dance Studio

(a) (*continued*) **Miscellaneous Expense** Account No.

Date 19XX		*Description*	*Post. Ref.*	*Debit**	*Credit*	*Balance*

(b)

Thorp Dance Studio
Trial Balance
June 30, 19XX

				Debit	*Credit*

Name ______________________

Section ______________________

2-26A
Thorp Dance Studio

(c)

Thorp Dance Studio
Income Statement
For the Month of June, 19XX

Revenue	
Expenses	

(d)

Thorp Dance Studio
Statement of Owner's Equity
For the Month of June, 19XX

Name ______________________

Section ______________________

2-26A
Thorp Dance Studio

Thorp Dance Studio
Balance Sheet
June 30, 19XX

(e)

Assets		Liabilities	
		Owner's Equity	

Name ______________________________

Section ______________________________

2-27A

Cardinal, Inc.

(a)

Cash — Account No.

Date 19XX		Description	Post. Ref.	Debit*	Credit	Balance

Accounts Receivable — Account No.

Date 19XX		Description	Post. Ref.	Debit*	Credit	Balance

Supplies on Hand — Account No.

Date 19XX		Description	Post. Ref.	Debit*	Credit	Balance

Name ____________________

Section ____________________

2-27A

Cardinal, Inc.

(a) *(continued)*

Office Furniture and Equipment Account No.

Date 19XX		Description	Post. Ref.	Debit*	Credit	Balance

Notes Payable Account No.

Date 19XX		Description	Post. Ref.	Debit	Credit*	Balance

Accounts Payable Account No.

Date 19XX		Description	Post. Ref.	Debit	Credit*	Balance

Capital Stock Account No.

Date 19XX		Description	Post. Ref.	Debit	Credit*	Balance

Name

Section

2-27A

Cardinal, Inc.

(a) *(continued)*

Advertising Revenue Account No.

Date 19XX		Description	Post. Ref.	Debit	Credit*	Balance

Want Ad Revenue Account No.

Date 19XX		Description	Post. Ref.	Debit	Credit*	Balance

Printing Expense Account No.

Date 19XX		Description	Post. Ref.	Debit*	Credit	Balance

Mailing Expense Account No.

Date 19XX		Description	Post. Ref.	Debit*	Credit	Balance

Name ______________________________

Section ______________________________

2-27A

Cardinal, Inc.

(a) *(continued)*

Utilities Expense — **Account No.**

Date 19XX		*Description*	*Post. Ref.*	*Debit**	*Credit*	*Balance*

Salaries Expense — **Account No.**

Date 19XX		*Description*	*Post. Ref.*	*Debit**	*Credit*	*Balance*

Rent Expense — **Account No.**

Date 19XX		*Description*	*Post. Ref.*	*Debit**	*Credit*	*Balance*

Delivery Expense — **Account No.**

Date 19XX		*Description*	*Post. Ref.*	*Debit**	*Credit*	*Balance*

Name ______________________

Section ______________________

2-27A

Cardinal, Inc.

Cardinal, Inc.
Trial Balance
December 31, 19XX

(b)

			Debit	Credit

(c)

(d)

Name ____________________

Section ____________________

2-28A

Bell Tree Service

Bell Tree Service
Corrected Trial Balance
May 31, 19XX

			Debit	Credit

Name ______________________

Section ______________________

Chapter 2
Business Decision Problem
Sunset Picture Gallery

(a)

(b)

Name ______________________

Section ______________________

3-26

Ruff Roofing Service

(a)

General Journal

Page 1

Date 19XX		Description	Post. Ref.	Debit	Credit

Name ____________________

Section ____________________

3-26

Ruff Roofing Service

(a) *(continued)*

[(b), (c) are on pp. 75–79; (d) is on p. 80]

General Journal

Page 2

Date 19XX		*Description*	*Post. Ref.*	*Debit*	*Credit*
(e)		*[(e) is also on pp. 75–79]*			

Name ______________________________

Section ______________________________

Ruff Roofing Service

(b), (c), and (e)

[(d) is on p. 80]

Date 19XX	Description	Post. Ref.	Debit	Credit	Balance

Date 19XX	Description	Post. Ref.	Debit	Credit	Balance

Date 19XX	Description	Post. Ref.	Debit	Credit	Balance

Name ______________________

Section ______________________

3-26

Ruff Roofing Service

(b), (c), and (e) (*continued*)

[(d) is on p. 80]

Date 19XX		Description	Post. Ref.	Debit	Credit	Balance

Date 19XX		Description	Post. Ref.	Debit	Credit	Balance

Date 19XX		Description	Post. Ref.	Debit	Credit	Balance

Date 19XX		Description	Post. Ref.	Debit	Credit	Balance

Name ______________________

Section ______________________

3-26

Ruff Roofing Service

(b), (c), and (e) (*continued*)

[(d) is on p. 80]

Date 19XX		Description	Post. Ref.	Debit	Credit	Balance

Date 19XX		Description	Post. Ref.	Debit	Credit	Balance

Date 19XX		Description	Post. Ref.	Debit	Credit	Balance

Date 19XX		Description	Post. Ref.	Debit	Credit	Balance

Name ______________________________

Section ______________________________

3-26

Ruff Roofing Service

(b), (c), and (e) (*continued*)

[(d) is on p. 80]

Date 19XX		Description	Post. Ref.	Debit	Credit	Balance

Date 19XX		Description	Post. Ref.	Debit	Credit	Balance

Date 19XX		Description	Post. Ref.	Debit	Credit	Balance

Date 19XX		Description	Post. Ref.	Debit	Credit	Balance

Name ______________________________

Section ______________________________

3-26

Ruff Roofing Service

(b), (c), and (e) ***(continued)***

[(d) is on p. 80]

Date 19XX		Description	Post. Ref.	Debit	Credit	Balance

Date 19XX		Description	Post. Ref.	Debit	Credit	Balance

Date 19XX		Description	Post. Ref.	Debit	Credit	Balance

Date 19XX		Description	Post. Ref.	Debit	Credit	Balance

Name ______________________

Section ______________________

Ruff Roofing Service
Trial Balance
April 30, 19XX

(d)

			Debit	*Credit*

Name ____________________

Section ____________________

3-27

Benson Carpet Cleaners

General Journal

Date 19XX		Description	Post. Ref.	Debit	Credit

Name ______________________

Section ______________________

Phototake, Inc.
Trial Balance
December 31, 19XX

(a)

			Debit	Credit

Name ______________________________

Section ______________________________

3-28

Phototake, Inc.

(b)

General Journal

Date 19XX		Description	Post. Ref.	Debit	Credit

Name ______________________________

Section ______________________________

3-29

Complete Catering Service

(a), (b), and (d)

[(b) is also on pp. 91–92; (c) is on p. 93;
(d) is also on p. 94]

Cash — **Account No. 11**

Date 19XX		Description	Post. Ref.	Debit*	Credit	Balance

Accounts Receivable — **Account No. 12**

Date 19XX		Description	Post. Ref.	Debit*	Credit	Balance

Supplies on Hand — **Account No. 13**

Date 19XX		Description	Post. Ref.	Debit*	Credit	Balance

Name ____________________

Section ____________________

3-29
Complete Catering Service

(a), (b), and (d) (*continued*)
[(b) is also on pp. 91–92; (c) is on p. 93; (d) is also on p. 94]

Prepaid Rent — Account No. 14

Date 19XX		Description	Post. Ref.	Debit*	Credit	Balance

Prepaid Insurance — Account No. 15

Date 19XX		Description	Post. Ref.	Debit*	Credit	Balance

Delivery Van — Account No. 16

Date 19XX		Description	Post. Ref.	Debit*	Credit	Balance

Accumulated Depreciation—Delivery Van — Account No. 17

Date 19XX		Description	Post. Ref.	Debit	Credit*	Balance

Name ______________________

Section ______________________

Complete Catering Service

(a), (b), and (d) (*continued*)

[(b) is also on pp. 91–92; (c) is on p. 93;
(d) is also on p. 94]

Equipment — **Account No. 18**

Date 19XX		Description	Post. Ref.	Debit*	Credit	Balance

Accumulated Depreciation—Equipment — **Account No. 19**

Date 19XX		Description	Post. Ref.	Debit	Credit*	Balance

Accounts Payable — **Account No. 21**

Date 19XX		Description	Post. Ref.	Debit	Credit*	Balance

Wages Payable — **Account No. 22**

Date 19XX		Description	Post. Ref.	Debit	Credit*	Balance

Name ______________________

Section ______________________

3-29

Complete Catering Service

(a), (b), and (d) (*continued*)

[(b) is also on pp. 91–92; (c) is on p. 93;
(d) is also on p. 94]

Unearned Catering Fees — **Account No. 23**

Date 19XX		Description	Post. Ref.	Debit	Credit*	Balance

H. Field, Capital — **Account No. 31**

Date 19XX		Description	Post. Ref.	Debit	Credit*	Balance

H. Field, Drawing — **Account No. 32**

Date 19XX		Description	Post. Ref.	Debit*	Credit	Balance

Catering Fees Revenue — **Account No. 41**

Date 19XX		Description	Post. Ref.	Debit	Credit*	Balance

Name ______________________

Section ______________________

3-29

Complete Catering Service

(a), (b), and (d) (*continued*)

[(b) is also on pp. 91–92; (c) is on p. 93; (d) is also on p. 94]

Wages Expense — **Account No. 51**

Date 19XX		Description	Post. Ref.	Debit*	Credit	Balance

Rent Expense — **Account No. 52**

Date 19XX		Description	Post. Ref.	Debit*	Credit	Balance

Supplies Expense — **Account No. 53**

Date 19XX		Description	Post. Ref.	Debit*	Credit	Balance

Insurance Expense — **Account No. 54**

Date 19XX		Description	Post. Ref.	Debit*	Credit	Balance

Name ______________________

Section ______________________

3-29
Complete Catering Service

(a), (b), and (d) (*continued*)
[(b) is also on pp. 91–92; (c) is on p. 93;
(d) is also on p. 94]

Delivery Van Expense — **Account No. 55**

Date 19XX		Description	Post. Ref.	Debit*	Credit	Balance

Depreciation Expense—Delivery Van — **Account No. 56**

Date 19XX		Description	Post. Ref.	Debit*	Credit	Balance

Depreciation Expense—Equipment — **Account No. 57**

Date 19XX		Description	Post. Ref.	Debit*	Credit	Balance

Name ______________________

Section ______________________

3-29

Complete Catering Service

(b) **General Journal** Page 1

Date 19XX		Description	Post. Ref.	Debit	Credit

Name ______________________________

Section ______________________________

3-29

Complete Catering Service

(b) ***(continued)***

General Journal

Page 2

Date 19XX		Description	Post. Ref.	Debit	Credit

Name ______________________________

Section ______________________________

Complete Catering Service
Trial Balance
July 31, 19XX

(c)

			Debit	Credit

Name ______________________

Section ______________________

3-29

Complete Catering Service

(d)

General Journal

Page 3

Date 19XX		Description	Post. Ref.	Debit	Credit

Name ______________________________

Section ______________________________

3-30

Quality Print

General Journal

Date 19XX		Description	Post. Ref.	Debit	Credit

Name ______________________________

Section ______________________________

3-31

Harmonic Music Society

(a)

General Journal

Date 19XX	Description	Post. Ref.	Debit	Credit

(b)

(c)

(d)

Name ______________________________

Section ______________________________

3-26A

Lin Karate School

(a) **General Journal** Page 1

Date 19XX		Description	Post. Ref.	Debit	Credit

Name ______________________

Section ______________________

3-26A

Lin Karate School

(a) (*continued*)

[(b), (c) are on pp. 101–105; (d) is on p. 106]

General Journal

Page 2

Date 19XX		Description	Post. Ref.	Debit	Credit
(e)		[(e) is also on pp. 101–105]			

Name ______________________

Section ______________________

3-26A

Lin Karate School

(b), (c), and (e)

[(d) is on p. 106]

Date 19XX		Description	Post. Ref.	Debit	Credit	Balance

Date 19XX		Description	Post. Ref.	Debit	Credit	Balance

Date 19XX		Description	Post. Ref.	Debit	Credit	Balance

Name ____________________

Section ____________________

3-26A

Lin Karate School

(b), (c), and (e) (*continued*)

[(d) is on p. 106]

Date 19XX		Description	Post. Ref.	Debit	Credit	Balance

Date 19XX		Description	Post. Ref.	Debit	Credit	Balance

Date 19XX		Description	Post. Ref.	Debit	Credit	Balance

Date 19XX		Description	Post. Ref.	Debit	Credit	Balance

Name ______________________________

Section ______________________________

3-26A

Lin Karate School

(b), (c), and (e) (*continued*)

[(d) is on p. 106]

Date 19XX		Description	Post. Ref.	Debit	Credit	Balance

Date 19XX		Description	Post. Ref.	Debit	Credit	Balance

Date 19XX		Description	Post. Ref.	Debit	Credit	Balance

Date 19XX		Description	Post. Ref.	Debit	Credit	Balance

Name ______________________

Section ______________________

3-26A

Lin Karate School

(b), (c), and (e) (*continued*)

[(d) is on p. 106]

Date 19XX		Description	Post. Ref.	Debit	Credit	Balance

Date 19XX		Description	Post. Ref.	Debit	Credit	Balance

Date 19XX		Description	Post. Ref.	Debit	Credit	Balance

Date 19XX		Description	Post. Ref.	Debit	Credit	Balance

Name ______________________

Section ______________________

3-26A

Lin Karate School

(b), (c), and (e) (*continued*)

[(d) is on p. 106]

Date 19XX		Description	Post. Ref.	Debit	Credit	Balance

Date 19XX		Description	Post. Ref.	Debit	Credit	Balance

Date 19XX		Description	Post. Ref.	Debit	Credit	Balance

Name ______________________________

Section ______________________________

3-26A
Lin Karate School

(d)

Lin Karate School
Trial Balance
June 30, 19XX

			Debit	Credit

Name ______________________

Section ______________________

3-27A

The Wheel House, Inc.

General Journal

Date 19XX		Description	Post. Ref.	Debit	Credit

Name ______________________________

Section ______________________________

3-28A
Deliverit

Deliverit
Trial Balance
(a) **December 31, 19XX**

			Debit	Credit

Name ____________________

Section ____________________

3-28A
Deliverit

(b)

General Journal

Date 19XX		Description	Post. Ref.	Debit	Credit

Name ____________________

Section ____________________

3-29A
Market-Touch

(a), (b), and (d)

[(b) is also on pp. 116–117; (c) is on p. 118; (d) is also on p. 119]

Cash — **Account No. 11**

Date 19XX		Description	Post. Ref.	Debit*	Credit	Balance

Accounts Receivable — **Account No. 12**

Date 19XX		Description	Post. Ref.	Debit*	Credit	Balance

Office Supplies on Hand — **Account No. 14**

Date 19XX		Description	Post. Ref.	Debit*	Credit	Balance

Name ______________________

Section ______________________

3-29A
Market-Touch

(a), (b), and (d) (*continued*)

[(b) is also on pp. 116–117; (c) is on p. 118; (d) is also on p. 119]

Prepaid Advertising — **Account No. 15**

Date 19XX		Description	Post. Ref.	Debit*	Credit	Balance

Office Equipment — **Account No. 16**

Date 19XX		Description	Post. Ref.	Debit*	Credit	Balance

Accumulated Depreciation—Office Equipment — **Account No. 17**

Date 19XX		Description	Post. Ref.	Debit	Credit*	Balance

Accounts Payable — **Account No. 21**

Date 19XX		Description	Post. Ref.	Debit	Credit*	Balance

Name ______________________

Section ______________________

3-29A

Market-Touch

(a), (b), and (d) (*continued*)
[(b) is also on pp. 116–117; (c) is on p. 118;
(d) is also on p. 119]

Salaries Payable — **Account No. 22**

Date 19XX		Description	Post. Ref.	Debit	Credit*	Balance

Unearned Service Fees — **Account No. 23**

Date 19XX		Description	Post. Ref.	Debit	Credit*	Balance

J. Austin, Capital — **Account No. 31**

Date 19XX		Description	Post. Ref.	Debit	Credit*	Balance

J. Austin, Drawing — **Account No. 32**

Date 19XX		Description	Post. Ref.	Debit*	Credit	Balance

Name ______________________________

Section ______________________________

3-29A

Market-Touch

(a), (b), and (d) (*continued*)

[(b) is also on pp. 116–117; (c) is on p. 118;
(d) is also on p. 119]

Service Fees Earned — **Account No. 41**

Date 19XX		Description	Post. Ref.	Debit	Credit*	Balance

Salaries Expense — **Account No. 51**

Date 19XX		Description	Post. Ref.	Debit*	Credit	Balance

Advertising Expense — **Account No. 52**

Date 19XX		Description	Post. Ref.	Debit*	Credit	Balance

Supplies Expense — **Account No. 53**

Date 19XX		Description	Post. Ref.	Debit*	Credit	Balance

Name ____________________

Section ____________________

3-29A
Market-Touch

(a), (b), and (d) (*continued*)

[(b) is also on pp. 116–117; (c) is on p. 118;
(d) is also on p. 119]

Rent Expense — **Account No. 54**

Date 19XX		*Description*	*Post. Ref.*	*Debit**	*Credit*	*Balance*

Travel Expense — **Account No. 55**

Date 19XX		*Description*	*Post. Ref.*	*Debit**	*Credit*	*Balance*

Depreciation Expense—Office Equipment — **Account No. 56**

Date 19XX		*Description*	*Post. Ref.*	*Debit**	*Credit*	*Balance*

Postage Expense — **Account No. 57**

Date 19XX		*Description*	*Post. Ref.*	*Debit**	*Credit*	*Balance*

Name ______________________

Section ______________________

3-29A
Market-Touch

(b) **General Journal** Page 1

Date 19XX		Description	Post. Ref.	Debit	Credit

Name ____________________

Section ____________________

3-29A

Market-Touch

(b) *(continued)* **General Journal** Page 2

Date 19XX		Description	Post. Ref.	Debit	Credit

Name ______________________

Section ______________________

3-29A
Market-Touch

Market-Touch
Trial Balance
June 30, 19XX

(c)

				Debit	Credit

Name ______________________

Section ______________________

3-29A

Market-Touch

(d) **General Journal** Page 3

Date 19XX		Description	Post. Ref.	Debit	Credit

Name ______________________

Section ______________________

3-30A
Water Guard

General Journal

Date 19XX		Description	Post. Ref.	Debit	Credit

Name ______________________

Section ______________________

3-31A

Adjustments to Unrelated Accounts

General Journal

Page 1

Date 19XX		Description	Post. Ref.	Debit	Credit

Name ____________________

Section ____________________

3-31A

Adjustments to Unrelated Accounts

(continued)

General Journal

Page 2

Date 19XX		Description	Post. Ref.	Debit	Credit

Name ______________________

Section ______________________

Name ______________________

Section ______________________

4-28

Lane Cleaning Service

(b)
[(a) is in foldout section]

General Journal

Date 19XX		Description	Post. Ref.	Debit	Credit
		Closing Entries			

Name ______________________

Section ______________________

4-30

Custom Upholstery Service, Inc.

Custom Upholstery Service, Inc.
Worksheet
For the Year Ended December 31, 19XX

(a)

Description	Trial Balance Debit	Trial Balance Credit	Adjustments Debit	Adjustments Credit	Adjusted Trial Balance Debit	Adjusted Trial Balance Credit
Cash	2500				2500	
Accounts Receivable	4615				4615	
Prepaid Rent	1875				1250	
Supplies on Hand	12360				5240	
Equipment	22000				22000	
Accumulated Depreciation		5250				7875
Accounts Payable		1300				1300
Unearned Service Fees		800				200
Capital Stock		10000				10000
Retained Earnings		9475				9475
Service Fees Earned		32140				32740
Wages Expense	6500				7070	
Utilities Expense	2240				2500	
Rent Expense	6875				7500	
	58965	58965				
Supplies Expense					7120	
Depreciation Expense					2625	
Wages Payable						570
Utilities Payable						260
			11800	11800	62420	62420

Name ______________________________

Section ______________________________

4-30

Custom Upholstery Service, Inc.

(a) (*continued*)

General Journal

Date 19XX		Description	Post. Ref.	Debit	Credit

Name ____________________

Section ____________________

4-30

Custom Upholstery Service, Inc.

(b)

	Income Statement	Balance Sheet

Name ______________________

Section ______________________

4-31

Foster Freight Service

(b)

[(a) is in foldout section]

Foster Freight Service
Income Statement
For the Year Ended December 31, 19X1

Revenue	
Expenses	

Foster Freight Service
Statement of Owner's Equity
For the Year Ended December 31, 19X1

Name ____________________

Section ____________________

4-31
Foster Freight Service

Foster Freight Service
Balance Sheet
December 31, 19X1

(b) (*continued*)

Assets		*Liabilities*	
		Owner's Equity	

Name ______________________

Section ______________________

4-31
Foster Freight Service

(c)

General Journal

Date 19XX		Description	Post. Ref.	Debit	Credit

Name ____________________

Section ____________________

4-32

Ken Howard, Tax Consultant

(e) *(continued)*

General Journal

Page 4

Date 19XX		Description	Post. Ref.	Debit	Credit

Ken Howard, Tax Consultant
Post-closing Trial Balance
December 31, 19XX

(f)

				Debit	Credit

Name ______________________

Section ______________________

4-32

Ken Howard, Tax Consultant

(g)

Page 5

Date 19X1	Description	Post. Ref.	Debit	Credit

Name ______________________

Section ______________________

4-33

Sanstar, Inc.

(a)

General Journal

Date 19XX		Description	Post. Ref.	Debit	Credit

(b)

(c)

Name ____________________

Section ____________________

4-34

Corey Company

(a)

General Journal

Date 19XX		Description	Post. Ref.	Debit	Credit

(b)

Date 19XX		Description	Post. Ref.	Debit	Credit

Name ____________________

Section ____________________

4-34

Corey Company

(c)

General Journal

Date 19X6		Description	Post. Ref.	Debit	Credit
(d)					

Name ______________________

Section ______________________

4-28A

Careful Moving Service

(b)
[(a) is in foldout section]

General Journal

Date 19XX		Description	Post. Ref.	Debit	Credit

Name ____________________

Section ____________________

4-29A
Superior Outfitters

(b)
[(a) is in foldout section]

Superior Outfitters
Income Statement
For the Three Months Ended July 31, 19XX

Revenue		
Expenses		

Superior Outfitters
Statement of Owner's Equity
For the Three Months Ended July 31, 19XX

Name ______________________

Section ______________________

4-29A
Superior Outfitters

(b) (continued)

Superior Outfitters
Balance Sheet
July 31, 19XX

Assets			Liabilities		
			Owner's Equity		

Name ______________________

Section ______________________

4-30A

Linn Refinishing Service

(a)

Name ______________________

Section ______________________

4-30A
Linn Refinishing Service

(b)

Linn Refinishing Service
Worksheet
For the Year Ended December 31, 19XX

Description	Adjusted Trial Balance Debit	Adjusted Trial Balance Credit	Income Statement Debit	Income Statement Credit	Balance Sheet Debit	Balance Sheet Credit
Cash	400					
Accounts Receivable	860					
Prepaid Rent	620					
Supplies on Hand	780					
Equipment	4500					
Accounts Payable		290				
M. Linn, Capital		5300				
M. Linn, Drawing	2400					
Service Revenue		10150				
Wages Expense	3120					
Utilities Expense	840					
Rent Expense	1500					
Supplies Expense	930					
Depreciation Expense	450					
Accumulated Depreciation		450				
Wages Payable		120				
Utilities Payable		90				
	16400	16400				

Name ______________________

Section ______________________

4-31A

Glide and Stride, Inc.

Glide and Stride, Inc.
Income Statement
For the Year Ended December 31, 19X2

(b)

Revenue			
Expenses			

Name ______________________

Section ______________________

Glide and Stride, Inc.
Balance Sheet
December 31, 19X2

(b) (*continued*)

Assets		*Liabilities*	
		Stockholders' Equity	

Name ______________________________

Section ______________________________

4-31A

Glide and Stride, Inc.

(c)

General Journal

Date 19X2		Description	Post. Ref.	Debit	Credit

Name ______________________________ **4-32A**

Section ______________________________ Melissa Crane, Attorney

(a), (b), (e), and (g)

[(b) is also on pp. 170–71; (c) is in foldout section; (d) is on pp. 172–73;
(e) is also on pp. 174–75; (f) is on p. 175; (g) is also on p. 176]

Cash **Account No. 11**

Date 19XX		Description	Post. Ref.	Debit*	Credit	Balance

Accounts Receivable **Account No. 12**

Date 19XX		Description	Post. Ref.	Debit*	Credit	Balance

Prepaid Rent **Account No. 13**

Date 19XX		Description	Post. Ref.	Debit*	Credit	Balance

Name ______________________

Section ______________________

4-32A

Melissa Crane, Attorney

(a), (b), (e), and (g) (*continued*)

[(b) is also on pp. 170–71; (c) is in foldout section; (d) is on pp. 172–73; (c) is also on pp. 174–75; (f) is on p. 175; (g) is also on p. 176]

Supplies on Hand — **Account No. 14**

Date 19XX		Description	Post. Ref.	Debit*	Credit	Balance

Furniture and Fixtures — **Account No. 15**

Date 19XX		Description	Post. Ref.	Debit*	Credit	Balance

Accumulated Depreciation — **Account No. 16**

Date 19XX		Description	Post. Ref.	Debit	Credit*	Balance

Accounts Payable — **Account No. 21**

Date 19XX		Description	Post. Ref.	Debit	Credit*	Balance

Name ______________________

Section ______________________

4-32A

Melissa Crane, Attorney

(a), (b), (e), and (g) (*continued*)

[(b) is also on pp. 170–71; (c) is in foldout section; (d) is on pp. 172–73; (e) is also on pp. 174–75; (f) is on p. 175; (g) is also on p. 176]

Salary Payable — Account No. 22

Date 19XX		Description	Post. Ref.	Debit	Credit*	Balance

M. Crane, Capital — Account No. 31

Date 19XX		Description	Post. Ref.	Debit	Credit*	Balance

M. Crane, Drawing — Account No. 32

Date 19XX		Description	Post. Ref.	Debit*	Credit	Balance

Income Summary — Account No. 33

Date 19XX		Description	Post. Ref.	Debit	Credit*	Balance

Name ______________________

Section ______________________

4-32A

Melissa Crane, Attorney

(a), (b), (e), and (g) (*continued*)

[(b) is also on pp. 170–71; (c) is in foldout section; (d) is on pp. 172–73; (e) is also on pp. 174–75; (f) is on p. 175; (g) is also on p. 176]

Professional Fees Earned — **Account No. 41**

Date 19XX		Description	Post. Ref.	Debit	Credit*	Balance

Supplies Expense — **Account No. 51**

Date 19XX		Description	Post. Ref.	Debit*	Credit	Balance

Salary Expense — **Account No. 52**

Date 19XX		Description	Post. Ref.	Debit*	Credit	Balance

Rent Expense — **Account No. 53**

Date 19XX		Description	Post. Ref.	Debit*	Credit	Balance

Name ______________________

Section ______________________

4-32A

Melissa Crane, Attorney

(a), (b), (e), and (g) (*continued*)

[(b) is also on pp. 170–71; (c) is in foldout section; (d) is on pp. 172–73; (e) is also on pp. 174–75; (f) is on p. 175; (g) is also on p. 176]

Depreciation Expense **Account No. 54**

Date 19XX		Description	Post. Ref.	Debit*	Credit	Balance

Name ______________________

Section ______________________

4-32A

Melissa Crane, Attorney

(b)

General Journal

Page 1

Date 19XX		Description	Post. Ref.	Debit	Credit

Name ______________________________

Section ______________________________

4-32A

Melissa Crane, Attorney

(b) (*continued*) **General Journal** Page 2

Date 19XX		Description	Post. Ref.	Debit	Credit

Name ______________________

Section ______________________

4-32A

Melissa Crane, Attorney

Melissa Crane, Attorney
Income Statement
For the Month of December, 19XX

(d)

Revenue			
Expenses			

Melissa Crane, Attorney
Statement of Owner's Equity
For the Month of December, 19XX

Name ______________________

Section ______________________

(d) (continued)

Melissa Crane, Attorney
Balance Sheet
December 31, 19XX

Assets		Liabilities	
		Owner's Equity	

Name ______________________

Section ______________________

4-32A

Melissa Crane, Attorney

(e)

General Journal

Page 3

Date 19XX		Description	Post. Ref.	Debit	Credit

Name ______________________

Section ______________________

4-32A

Melissa Crane, Attorney

(e) (continued)

General Journal

Page 4

Date 19XX		Description	Post. Ref.	Debit	Credit

(f)

Melissa Crane, Attorney
Post-closing Trial Balance
December 31, 19XX

				Debit	Credit

Name ____________________

Section ____________________

4-32A

Melissa Crane, Attorney

(g) **General Journal** Page 5

Date 19X1		Description	Post. Ref.	Debit	Credit

Name ____________________

Section ____________________

4-33A

Action Engineering Services, Inc.

(b)
[(a) is in foldout section]

Action Engineering Services, Inc.
Income Statement
For the Four Months Ended April 30, 19X5

Revenue

Expenses

Name ____________________

Section ____________________

4-33A

Action Engineering Services, Inc.

(c)

Action Engineering Services, Inc.
Balance Sheet
April 30, 19X5

Assets			Liabilities		
			Stockholders' Equity		

Name ______________________

Section ______________________

4-34A

Quinn Company

(a)

General Journal

Date 19X1		Description	Post. Ref.	Debit	Credit

(b)

Date 19X1		Description	Post. Ref.	Debit	Credit

Name ______________________________

Section ______________________________

4-34A

Quinn Company

(c)

General Journal

Date 19X2		Description	Post. Ref.	Debit	Credit
(d)					

Name ______________________

Section ______________________

Chapter 4
Business Decision Problem
Lynn Stowe, Tennis Concession

General Journal

Page 1

Date 19XX	Description	Post. Ref.	Debit	Credit

Name ______________________

Section ______________________

Chapter 4
Business Decision Problem
Lynn Stowe, Tennis Concession

(continued)

General Journal

Page 2

Date 19XX		Description	Post. Ref.	Debit	Credit

Name ______________________

Section ______________________

(continued)

Cash

Accounts Receivable

Supplies on Hand

Equipment

Note Payable—Bank

Unearned Lesson Fees

Rent Payable

Utilities Payable

L. Stowe, Capital

L. Stowe, Drawing

Rental Fees Earned

Lesson Fees Earned

Equipment Expense

Supplies Expense

Utilities Expense

Interest Expense

Rent Expense

Wages Expense

Insurance Expense

Name ______________________

Section ______________________

Lynn Stowe, Tennis Concession
Income Statement
For the Three Months Ended August 31, 19XX

(continued)

Revenue			
Expenses			

Name ______________________

Section ______________________

Lynn Stowe, Tennis Concession
Balance Sheet
August 31, 19XX

(continued)

Assets		Liabilities	
		Owner's Equity	

Comments: By using $1,200 of her savings, Lynn relinquished the opportunity to earn $21 interest income on her savings ($1,200 × 0.07 × 3/12). Deducting this from the $4,710 income generated leaves $4,689 of earnings generated in the 780 hours (13 weeks at 60 hours) worked. The "average pay" was $6.01 per hour, a rate well above the minimum wage and her alternative summer opportunity. Nonfinancial considerations would include the entrepreneurial risks and responsibilities Lynn assumed, the managerial experiences acquired, and the opportunity to deal with the public as a businessperson.

Name ______________________

Section ______________________

5-27

Whelan Company
and Mann Stores, Inc.

(a)

On the books of
Whelan Company:
General Journal

Date 19XX		Description	Post. Ref.	Debit	Credit

Name ______________________

Section ______________________

5-27

Whelan Company
and Mann Stores, Inc.

(b)

On the books of
Mann Stores, Inc.:
General Journal

Date 19XX		Description	Post. Ref.	Debit	Credit

Name

Section

5-28

Melville Corporation

General Journal

Page 1

Date 19XX		Description	Post. Ref.	Debit	Credit

Name ______________________

Section ______________________

5-28

Melville Corporation

(continued)

General Journal

Page 2

Date 19XX		Description	Post. Ref.	Debit	Credit

Name ____________________

Section ____________________

Melville Corporation

(continued) **General Journal** Page 3

Date 19XX	Description	Post. Ref.	Debit	Credit

Name ______________________________

Section ______________________________

[5–29 is in foldout section]

(a)

Oakdale Wholesale Company
Income Statement
For the Month of March, 19XX

Name ______________________

Section ______________________

5-32

Conway, Inc.

Conway, Inc.
Income Statement
For the Year Ended December 31, 19XX

Name ______________________

Section ______________________

5-33

Wesley Sport Shop

(a)

(b)

	Income Statement		Balance Sheet	
	Debit	Credit	Debit	Credit
Incorrect totals given				
(1)				
(2)				
(3)				
(4)				
(5)				
Correct totals				
Correct net income				

Name ______________________

Section ______________________

5-27A

Fortune Distributing Company
and Cornwall, Inc.

On the books of
Fortune Distributing Company:

(a)

General Journal

Date 19XX		Description	Post. Ref.	Debit	Credit

Name ______________________________

Section ______________________________

5-27A

Fortune Distributing Company
and Cornwall, Inc.

(b)

**On the books of
Cornwall, Inc.:
General Journal**

Date 19XX		Description	Post. Ref.	Debit	Credit

Name ______________________

Section ______________________

5-28A

Dover Company

General Journal

Page 1

Date 19XX		Description	Post. Ref.	Debit	Credit

Name ______________________

Section ______________________

5-28A

Dover Company

(continued)

General Journal

Page 2

Date 19XX		Description	Post. Ref.	Debit	Credit

Name ______________________

Section ______________________

5-28A

Dover Company

(continued)

General Journal

Page 3

Date 19XX		Description	Post. Ref.	Debit	Credit

Name ______________________

Section ______________________

5-30A

Harper Trading Company

Harper Trading Company
Income Statement
For the Month of February, 19XX

[5–29A is in foldout section]

(a)

(b)

(c)

Name ____________________

Section ____________________

5-31A

Diamond Distributors

(b)

[(a) is in foldout section]

Diamond Distributors
Income Statement
For the Year Ended December 31, 19XX

Name ____________________

Section ____________________

5-31A

Diamond Distributors

Diamond Distributors
Balance Sheet
December 31, 19XX

(c)

Name ______________________

Section ______________________

5-31A

Diamond Distributors

(d)

General Journal

Page 1

Date 19XX		Description	Post. Ref.	Debit	Credit

Name ______________________

Section ______________________

5-31A
Diamond Distributors

(e)

General Journal

Page 2

Date 19XX		Description	Post. Ref.	Debit	Credit

Name ______________________

Section ______________________

5-31A
Diamond Distributors

(f) **General Journal** Page 3

Date 19XX		Description	Post. Ref.	Debit	Credit

Name ____________________

Section ____________________

5-32A

Nu-Art, Inc.

Nu-Art, Inc.
Income Statement
For the Year Ended December 31, 19XX

Name ____________________

Section ____________________

5-33A

Trent Specialty Shop

(a)

(b)	Income Statement		Balance Sheet	
	Debit	Credit	Debit	Credit
Incorrect totals given				
(1)				
(2)				
(3)				
(4)				
(5)				
Correct totals				
Correct net income				

Name ______________________

Section ______________________

Chapter 5
Business Decision Problem
Imperial Wholesalers

(a)

(b)

(c)

Name ______________________

Section ______________________

Yates Trading Company
Income Statement
For the Year Ended December 31, 19XX

[A–1 and A–2(a) are in foldout section.]

(b)

Name ____________________

Section ____________________

A-2

Yates Trading Company

Yates Trading Company
Balance Sheet
(c) **December 31, 19XX**

Name ______________________________

Section ______________________________

A-2

Yates Trading Company

(d) **General Journal** Page 1

Date 19XX		Description	Post. Ref.	Debit	Credit

Name ______________________

Section ______________________

A-2

Yates Trading Company

(e)

General Journal

Page 2

Date 19XX		Description	Post. Ref.	Debit	Credit

Name ____________________

Section ____________________

A-2

Yates Trading Company

(f) **General Journal** Page 3

Date 19X1		Description	Post. Ref.	Debit	Credit

Name ______________________________

Section ______________________________

A-4

Diamond Distributors

[A–3 and A–4(a) are in foldout section]

(b)

Diamond Distributors
Income Statement
For the Year Ended December 31, 19XX

Name ______________________

Section ______________________

A-4

Diamond Distributors

Diamond Distributors
Balance Sheet
December 31, 19XX

(c)

Name ______________________

Section ______________________

A-4

Diamond Distributors

(d)

General Journal

Page 1

Date 19XX		Description	Post. Ref.	Debit	Credit

Name ______________________

Section ______________________

A-4
Diamond Distributors

(e) **General Journal** Page 2

Date 19XX		Description	Post. Ref.	Debit	Credit

Name ______________________________

Section ______________________________

A-4

Diamond Distributors

(f) **General Journal** Page 3

Date 19XX		Description	Post. Ref.	Debit	Credit

Name ______________________

Section ______________________

6-23

Preston Company

(a)
[(a) is also in foldout section]

Sales Journal

Page 1

Date 19XX	Invoice No.	Account	Post. Ref.	Amount	

General Journal

Page 1

Date 19XX	Description	Post. Ref.	Debit	Credit

Name ____________________

Section ____________________

6-23

Preston Company

General Ledger

(b) and (c)

Cash — Account No. 11

Date 19XX		Description	Post. Ref.	Debit*	Credit	Balance

Notes Receivable — Account No. 15

Date 19XX		Description	Post. Ref.	Debit*	Credit	Balance

Accounts Receivable — Account No. 16

Date 19XX		Description	Post. Ref.	Debit*	Credit	Balance

Name ______________________________

Section ______________________________

6-23
Preston Company

General Ledger

(b) and (c) (*continued*)

H. Preston, Capital — **Account No. 31**

Date 19XX		Description	Post. Ref.	Debit	Credit*	Balance

Sales — **Account No. 41**

Date 19XX		Description	Post. Ref.	Debit	Credit*	Balance

Sales Returns and Allowances — **Account No. 42**

Date 19XX		Description	Post. Ref.	Debit*	Credit	Balance

Sales Discounts — **Account No. 43**

Date 19XX		Description	Post. Ref.	Debit*	Credit	Balance

Name ____________________

Section ____________________

6-23

Preston Company

Accounts Receivable Subsidiary Ledger

(b) and (c) (*continued*)

Grady, Inc.

Account No. 1

Date 19XX		Description	Post. Ref.	Debit	Credit	Balance

Lund, Inc.

Account No. 2

Date 19XX		Description	Post. Ref.	Debit	Credit	Balance

Smart, Inc.

Account No. 3

Date 19XX		Description	Post. Ref.	Debit	Credit	Balance

Tull Company

Account No. 4

Date 19XX		Description	Post. Ref.	Debit	Credit	Balance

Name ______________________________

Section ______________________________

6-23

Preston Company

Accounts Receivable Subsidiary Ledger

(b) and (c) (*continued*) **Young Company** **Account No. 5**

Date 19XX	Description	Post. Ref.	Debit	Credit	Balance

Preston Company
Schedule of Accounts Receivable
May 31, 19XX

(d)

Name ______________________

Section ______________________

6-24

Warner Company

(a)

Invoice Register

Page 1

Date 19XX	Account Credited	Post. Ref.	Accounts Payable Credit	Purchases Debit	Office Supplies on Hand Debit	Store Supplies on Hand Debit	Other Debits		
							Account	Post. Ref.	Amount

Name ____________________

Section ____________________

6-24

Warner Company

(a) (continued)

Cash Disbursements Journal

Page 1

Date 19XX	Check No.	Description	Cash Credit	Purchases Discounts Credit	Accounts Payable		Other Accounts			
					Post. Ref.	Debit	Account	Post. Ref.	Debit	Credit

Name ______________________

Section ______________________

6-24

Warner Company

(a) (*continued*)

General Journal

Page 1

Date 19XX		Description	Post. Ref.	Debit	Credit

Name ______________________

Section ______________________

6-24

Warner Company

General Ledger

(b) and (c)

Cash Account No. 11

Date 19XX		Description	Post. Ref.	Debit*	Credit	Balance

Office Supplies on Hand Account No. 15

Date 19XX		Description	Post. Ref.	Debit*	Credit	Balance

Store Supplies on Hand Account No. 16

Date 19XX		Description	Post. Ref.	Debit*	Credit	Balance

Delivery Equipment Account No. 17

Date 19XX		Description	Post. Ref.	Debit*	Credit	Balance

Name ______________________

Section ______________________

6-24

Warner Company

General Ledger

(b) and (c) (*continued*)

Office Equipment — Account No. 18

Date 19XX		Description	Post. Ref.	Debit*	Credit	Balance

Notes Payable — Account No. 21

Date 19XX		Description	Post. Ref.	Debit	Credit*	Balance

Accounts Payable — Account No. 22

Date 19XX		Description	Post. Ref.	Debit	Credit*	Balance

L. Warner, Drawing — Account No. 32

Date 19XX		Description	Post. Ref.	Debit*	Credit	Balance

Name ______________________

Section ______________________

6-24
Warner Company

General Ledger

(b) and (c) (*continued*)

Purchases

Account No. 51

Date 19XX		Description	Post. Ref.	Debit*	Credit	Balance

Purchases Returns and Allowances

Account No. 52

Date 19XX		Description	Post. Ref.	Debit	Credit*	Balance

Purchases Discounts

Account No. 53

Date 19XX		Description	Post. Ref.	Debit	Credit*	Balance

Transportation In

Account No. 54

Date 19XX		Description	Post. Ref.	Debit*	Credit	Balance

Name ______________________

Section ______________________

6-24
Warner Company

Accounts Payable Subsidary Ledger

(b) and (c) *(continued)*

Ford, Inc. Account No. 1

Date 19XX		Description	Post. Ref.	Debit	Credit	Balance

Gem Supply Company Account No. 2

Date 19XX		Description	Post. Ref.	Debit	Credit	Balance

Hahn, Inc. Account No. 3

Date 19XX		Description	Post. Ref.	Debit	Credit	Balance

Vine Company Account No. 4

Date 19XX		Description	Post. Ref.	Debit	Credit	Balance

Name ______________________

Section ______________________

6-24

Warner Company

(d)

Warner Company
Schedule of Accounts Payable
August 31, 19XX

Name ______________________

Section ______________________

6-25

Jordan Company

(a) and (b) (*continued*)
[(a) and (b) begin in foldout section]

Cash Disbursements Journal

Date 19XX	Check No.	Description	Cash Credit	Purchases Discounts Credit	Accounts Payable Post. Ref.	Accounts Payable Debit	Other Accounts Account	Other Accounts Post. Ref.	Other Accounts Debit	Other Accounts Credit
(b)		Column Totals	Debit	Credit						

Name ______________________

Section ______________________

6-26

Shannon Distributors

General Ledger

(a) and (d)

[(b) and more (d) are on pp. 259–60; (c) is on pp. 261–63 and in foldout section]

Cash — Account No. 11

Date 19XX		Description	Post. Ref.	Debit*	Credit	Balance

Accounts Receivable — Account No. 12

Date 19XX		Description	Post. Ref.	Debit*	Credit	Balance

Inventory — Account No. 14

Date 19XX		Description	Post. Ref.	Debit*	Credit	Balance

Store Supplies on Hand — Account No. 15

Date 19XX		Description	Post. Ref.	Debit*	Credit	Balance

Name ____________________

Section ____________________

Shannon Distributors

General Ledger

(a) and (d) (*continued*)

Office Supplies on Hand — Account No. 16

Date 19XX		Description	Post. Ref.	Debit*	Credit	Balance

Equipment — Account No. 17

Date 19XX		Description	Post. Ref.	Debit*	Credit	Balance

Accumulated Depreciation — Account No. 18

Date 19XX		Description	Post. Ref.	Debit	Credit*	Balance

Accounts Payable — Account No. 21

Date 19XX		Description	Post. Ref.	Debit	Credit*	Balance

Name ______________________

Section ______________________

6-26

Shannon Distributors

General Ledger

(a) and (d) (*continued*)

R. Shannon, Capital — Account No. 31

Date 19XX		Description	Post. Ref.	Debit	Credit*	Balance

R. Shannon, Drawing — Account No. 32

Date 19XX		Description	Post. Ref.	Debit*	Credit	Balance

Sales — Account No. 41

Date 19XX		Description	Post. Ref.	Debit	Credit*	Balance

Sales Returns and Allowances — Account No. 42

Date 19XX		Description	Post. Ref.	Debit*	Credit	Balance

Name

Section

6-26
Shannon Distributors

General Ledger

(a) and (d) *(continued)*

Sales Discounts
Account No. 43

Date 19XX		Description	Post. Ref.	Debit*	Credit	Balance

Miscellaneous Income
Account No. 44

Date 19XX		Description	Post. Ref.	Debit	Credit*	Balance

Purchases
Account No. 51

Date 19XX		Description	Post. Ref.	Debit*	Credit	Balance

Purchases Returns and Allowances
Account No. 52

Date 19XX		Description	Post. Ref.	Debit	Credit*	Balance

Name ______________________________

Section ______________________________

6-26
Shannon Distributors

General Ledger

(a) and (d) *(continued)*

Purchases Discounts
Account No. 53

Date 19XX		*Description*	*Post. Ref.*	*Debit*	*Credit**	*Balance*

Transportation In
Account No. 54

Date 19XX		*Description*	*Post. Ref.*	*Debit**	*Credit*	*Balance*

Rent Expense
Account No. 61

Date 19XX		*Description*	*Post. Ref.*	*Debit**	*Credit*	*Balance*

Salaries Expense
Account No. 62

Date 19XX		*Description*	*Post. Ref.*	*Debit**	*Credit*	*Balance*

General Ledger

(a) and (d) (*continued*)

Transportation Out — Account No. 63

Date 19XX		Description	Post. Ref.	Debit*	Credit	Balance

Miscellaneous Expense — Account No. 64

Date 19XX		Description	Post. Ref.	Debit*	Credit	Balance

Name ______________________________

Section ______________________________

6-26

Shannon Distributors

Accounts Receivable Subsidiary Ledger

(b) and (d)

Cooper Company

Account No. 1

Date 19XX		Description	Post. Ref.	Debit	Credit	Balance

Lyons, Inc.

Account No. 2

Date 19XX		Description	Post. Ref.	Debit	Credit	Balance

Thomas Company

Account No. 3

Date 19XX		Description	Post. Ref.	Debit	Credit	Balance

White Company

Account No. 4

Date 19XX		Description	Post. Ref.	Debit	Credit	Balance

Name ______________________

Section ______________________

6-26
Shannon Distributors

Accounts Payable Subsidiary Ledger

(b) and (d) (*continued*)

Davis Company — **Account No. 1**

Date 19XX		Description	Post. Ref.	Debit	Credit	Balance

Lenz Suppliers — **Account No. 2**

Date 19XX		Description	Post. Ref.	Debit	Credit	Balance

Sprague, Inc. — **Account No. 3**

Date 19XX		Description	Post. Ref.	Debit	Credit	Balance

Name ____________________

Section ____________________

6-26

Shannon Distributors

(c)
[(c) is also in foldouts]

Sales Journal

Page 1

Date 19XX		Invoice No.	Account	Post. Ref.	Amount	

General Journal

Page 1

Date 19XX		Description	Post. Ref.	Debit	Credit

Name ____________

Section ____________

6-26

Shannon Distributors

(c) (continued)

Invoice Register

Page 1

Date 19XX	Account Credited	Post. Ref.	Accounts Payable Credit	Purchases Debit	Office Supplies on Hand Debit	Store Supplies on Hand Debit	Other Debits		
							Account	Post. Ref.	Amount

Name ______________________

Section ______________________

6-26

Shannon Distributors

(c) ***(continued)***

Cash Disbursements Journal

Page 1

Date 19XX	Check No.	Description	Cash Credit	Purchases Discounts Credit	Accounts Payable		Other Accounts			
					Post. Ref.	Debit	Account	Post. Ref.	Debit	Credit

Name ______________________

Section ______________________

6-26

Shannon Distributors

Shannon Distributors
Trial Balance
October 31, 19XX

(e)

				Debit	Credit

Name ______________________

Section ______________________

Shannon Distributors
Schedule of Accounts Receivable
(f) **October 31, 19XX**

Shannon Distributors
Schedule of Accounts Payable
October 31, 19XX

Name ______________________________

Section ______________________________

6-28

Century, Inc.

General Ledger

[6–27 is in foldout section]

(a) and (b)

Cash in Bank

Account No. 11

Date 19XX		Description	Post. Ref.	Debit*	Credit	Balance

Office Supplies on Hand

Account No. 17

Date 19XX		Description	Post. Ref.	Debit*	Credit	Balance

Store Equipment

Account No. 18

Date 19XX		Description	Post. Ref.	Debit*	Credit	Balance

Vouchers Payable

Account No. 21

Date 19XX		Description	Post. Ref.	Debit	Credit*	Balance

Name ____________________

Section ____________________

6-28

Century, Inc.

General Ledger

(a) and (b) (*continued*)

Purchases — **Account No. 51**

Date 19XX		Description	Post. Ref.	Debit*	Credit	Balance

Purchases Returns and Allowances — **Account No. 52**

Date 19XX		Description	Post. Ref.	Debit	Credit*	Balance

Purchases Discounts — **Account No. 53**

Date 19XX		Description	Post. Ref.	Debit	Credit*	Balance

Transportation In — **Account No. 54**

Date 19XX		Description	Post. Ref.	Debit*	Credit	Balance

Name ______________________

Section ______________________

6-28

Century, Inc.

General Ledger

(a) and (b) (*continued*)

[(b) continues in foldout section before continuing on p. 270]

Rent Expense — **Account No. 61**

Date 19XX		Description	Post. Ref.	Debit*	Credit	Balance

Utilities Expense — **Account No. 62**

Date 19XX		Description	Post. Ref.	Debit*	Credit	Balance

(c)

Century, Inc.
Schedule of Unpaid Vouchers
June 30, 19XX

		Voucher No.	Name		Amount	

Name ____________________

Section ____________________

6-28

Century, Inc.

(b) (*continued*)

Century, Inc.
Check Register

Page 1

Check No.	Date	Payee	Voucher No.	Vouchers Payable Debit	Purchases Discounts Credit	Cash in Bank Credit

Name ______________________________

Section ______________________________

6-29

Bryant Company

(6–29 begins in foldout section)
(continued)

Bryant Company
Check Register

Page 1

Check No.	Date 19XX	Payee	Voucher No.	Vouchers Payable Debit	Purchases Discounts Credit	Cash in Bank Credit

Name ______________________

Section ______________________

6-23A
Matson Sales Company

(a)
[(a) is also in foldout section]

Sales Journal

Page 1

Date 19XX		Invoice No.	Account	Post. Ref.	Amount	

General Journal

Page 1

Date 19XX		Description	Post. Ref.	Debit	Credit

Name ______________________

Section ______________________

6-23A

Matson Sales Company

General Ledger

(b) and (c)

Cash — **Account No. 11**

Date 19XX		Description	Post. Ref.	Debit*	Credit	Balance

Notes Receivable — **Account No. 15**

Date 19XX		Description	Post. Ref.	Debit*	Credit	Balance

Accounts Receivable — **Account No. 16**

Date 19XX		Description	Post. Ref.	Debit*	Credit	Balance

C. Matson, Capital — **Account No. 31**

Date 19XX		Description	Post. Ref.	Debit	Credit*	Balance

Name ____________________

Section ____________________

6-23A

Matson Sales Company

General Ledger

(b) and (c) (*continued*)

Sales

Account No. 41

Date 19XX		Description	Post. Ref.	Debit	Credit*	Balance

Sales Returns and Allowances

Account No. 42

Date 19XX		Description	Post. Ref.	Debit*	Credit	Balance

Sales Discounts

Account No. 43

Date 19XX		Description	Post. Ref.	Debit*	Credit	Balance

Name ______________________

Section ______________________

6-23A

Matson Sales Company

Accounts Receivable Subsidiary Ledger

(b) and (c) (*continued*)

Carr, Inc. **Account No. 1**

Date 19XX		Description	Post. Ref.	Debit	Credit	Balance

Lynch Company **Account No. 2**

Date 19XX		Description	Post. Ref.	Debit	Credit	Balance

Pearson Company **Account No. 3**

Date 19XX		Description	Post. Ref.	Debit	Credit	Balance

M. Stone, Inc. **Account No. 4**

Date 19XX		Description	Post. Ref.	Debit	Credit	Balance

Name ______________________

Section ______________________

6-23A
Matson Sales Company

Accounts Receivable Subsidiary Ledger

(b) and (c) (*continued*) **J. Winslow** **Account No. 5**

Date 19XX		Description	Post. Ref.	Debit	Credit	Balance

(d)

Matson Sales Company
Schedule of Accounts Receivable
May 31, 19XX

Name ______________

Section ______________

6-24A
Domino Distributors

(a) and (c)
[(b) is on pp. 282–85]

Invoice Register

Page 1

Date 19XX	Account Credited	Post. Ref.	Accounts Payable Credit	Purchases Debit	Office Supplies on Hand Debit	Store Supplies on Hand Debit	Other Debits		
							Account	Post. Ref.	Amount

Name ______________________

Section ______________________

6-24A

Domino Distributors

(a) and (c) *(continued)*

Cash Disbursements Journal

Page 1

Date 19XX	Check No.	Description	Cash Credit	Purchases Discounts Credit	Accounts Payable		Other Accounts			
					Post. Ref.	Debit	Account	Post. Ref.	Debit	Credit

Name ____________________

Section ____________________

6-24A

Domino Distributors

(a) and (c) (*continued*) **General Journal** Page 1

Date 19XX		Description	Post. Ref.	Debit	Credit

Name ____________________

Section ____________________

6-24A

Domino Distributors

General Ledger

(b) and (c)

Cash — **Account No. 11**

Date 19XX		Description	Post. Ref.	Debit*	Credit	Balance

Office Supplies on Hand — **Account No. 15**

Date 19XX		Description	Post. Ref.	Debit*	Credit	Balance

Store Supplies on Hand — **Account No. 16**

Date 19XX		Description	Post. Ref.	Debit*	Credit	Balance

Delivery Equipment — **Account No. 17**

Date 19XX		Description	Post. Ref.	Debit*	Credit	Balance

Name ______________________

Section ______________________

6-24A

Domino Distributors

General Ledger

(b) and (c) (*continued*)

Office Equipment — **Account No. 18**

Date 19XX		Description	Post. Ref.	Debit*	Credit	Balance

Notes Payable — **Account No. 21**

Date 19XX		Description	Post. Ref.	Debit	Credit*	Balance

Accounts Payable — **Account No. 22**

Date 19XX		Description	Post. Ref.	Debit	Credit*	Balance

G. Domino, Drawing — **Account No. 32**

Date 19XX		Description	Post. Ref.	Debit*	Credit	Balance

Name ______________________

Section ______________________

6-24A

Domino Distributors

General Ledger

(b) and (c) (*continued*)

Purchases

Account No. 51

Date 19XX		Description	Post. Ref.	Debit*	Credit	Balance

Purchases Returns and Allowances

Account No. 52

Date 19XX		Description	Post. Ref.	Debit	Credit*	Balance

Purchases Discounts

Account No. 53

Date 19XX		Description	Post. Ref.	Debit	Credit*	Balance

Transportation In

Account No. 54

Date 19XX		Description	Post. Ref.	Debit*	Credit	Balance

Name ______________________

Section ______________________

6-24A

Domino Distributors

Accounts Payable Subsidiary Ledger

(b) and (c) (*continued*)

Beyer, Inc.

Account No. 1

Date 19XX		Description	Post. Ref.	Debit	Credit	Balance

Cole Supply Company

Account No. 2

Date 19XX		Description	Post. Ref.	Debit	Credit	Balance

Gibson Company

Account No. 3

Date 19XX		Description	Post. Ref.	Debit	Credit	Balance

Ryan, Inc.

Account No. 4

Date 19XX		Description	Post. Ref.	Debit	Credit	Balance

Name ____________________

Section ____________________

6-24A

Domino Distributors

Domino Distributors
Schedule of Accounts Payable
June 30, 19XX

(d)

Name ______________________

Section ______________________

6-25A

Crane Wholesalers

[(a) and (b) begin in foldout section]

(a) and (b) (*continued*)

Cash Disbursements Journal

Page 1

Date 19XX	Check No.	Description	Cash Credit	Purchases Discounts Credit	Accounts Payable Post. Ref.	Accounts Payable Debit	Other Accounts	Other Accounts Post. Ref.	Other Accounts Debit	Other Accounts Credit
(b)		Column Totals	Debit	Credit						

Name ______________________________

Section ______________________________

6-26A

Reed Wholesalers

(a) and (d)

[(b) and more (d) are on pp. 295–96. (c) is on pp. 297–99 and in foldout section]

General Ledger

Cash

Account No. 11

Date 19XX		Description	Post. Ref.	Debit*	Credit	Balance

Accounts Receivable

Account No. 12

Date 19XX		Description	Post. Ref.	Debit*	Credit	Balance

Inventory

Account No. 14

Date 19XX		Description	Post. Ref.	Debit*	Credit	Balance

Store Supplies on Hand

Account No. 15

Date 19XX		Description	Post. Ref.	Debit*	Credit	Balance

Name ______________________

Section ______________________

6-26A

Reed Wholesalers

General Ledger

(a) and (d) (*continued*)

Office Supplies on Hand — Account No. 16

Date 19XX		Description	Post. Ref.	Debit*	Credit	Balance

Equipment — Account No. 17

Date 19XX		Description	Post. Ref.	Debit*	Credit	Balance

Accumulated Depreciation — Account No. 18

Date 19XX		Description	Post. Ref.	Debit	Credit*	Balance

Accounts Payable — Account No. 21

Date 19XX		Description	Post. Ref.	Debit	Credit*	Balance

Name

Section

6-26A
Reed Wholesalers

General Ledger

(a) and (d) (*continued*)

F. Reed, Capital
Account No. 31

Date 19XX		Description	Post. Ref.	Debit	Credit*	Balance

F. Reed, Drawing
Account No. 32

Date 19XX		Description	Post. Ref.	Debit*	Credit	Balance

Sales
Account No. 41

Date 19XX		Description	Post. Ref.	Debit	Credit*	Balance

Sales Returns and Allowances
Account No. 42

Date 19XX		Description	Post. Ref.	Debit*	Credit	Balance

Name ______________________

Section ______________________

6-26A
Reed Wholesalers

General Ledger

(a) and (d) (*continued*)

Sales Discounts

Account No. 43

Date 19XX		Description	Post. Ref.	Debit*	Credit	Balance

Miscellaneous Income

Account No. 44

Date 19XX		Description	Post. Ref.	Debit	Credit*	Balance

Purchases

Account No. 51

Date 19XX		Description	Post. Ref.	Debit*	Credit	Balance

Purchases Returns and Allowances

Account No. 52

Date 19XX		Description	Post. Ref.	Debit	Credit*	Balance

Name ______________________

Section ______________________

6-26A
Reed Wholesalers

General Ledger

(a) and (d) (*continued*)

Purchases Discounts

Account No. 53

Date 19XX		Description	Post. Ref.	Debit	Credit*	Balance

Transportation In

Account No. 54

Date 19XX		Description	Post. Ref.	Debit*	Credit	Balance

Rent Expense

Account No. 61

Date 19XX		Description	Post. Ref.	Debit*	Credit	Balance

Salaries Expense

Account No. 62

Date 19XX		Description	Post. Ref.	Debit*	Credit	Balance

Name ______________________

Section ______________________

6-26A
Reed Wholesalers

General Ledger

(a) and (d) (*continued*)

Transportation Out — Account No. 63

Date 19XX		Description	Post. Ref.	Debit*	Credit	Balance

Miscellaneous Expense — Account No. 64

Date 19XX		Description	Post. Ref.	Debit*	Credit	Balance

Name ______________________________

Section ______________________________

6-26A

Reed Wholesalers

Accounts Receivable Subsidiary Ledger

(b) and (d)

Birch Company — **Account No. 1**

Date 19XX		Description	Post. Ref.	Debit	Credit	Balance

Judd, Inc. — **Account No. 2**

Date 19XX		Description	Post. Ref.	Debit	Credit	Balance

Murray Company — **Account No. 3**

Date 19XX		Description	Post. Ref.	Debit	Credit	Balance

Rodgers Distributors — **Account No. 4**

Date 19XX		Description	Post. Ref.	Debit	Credit	Balance

Name ______________________

Section ______________________

6-26A
Reed Wholesalers

Accounts Payable Subsidiary Ledger

(b) and (d) (*continued*)

Blair Company — Account No. 1

Date 19XX		Description	Post. Ref.	Debit	Credit	Balance

Gabriel Suppliers — Account No. 2

Date 19XX		Description	Post. Ref.	Debit	Credit	Balance

Simon, Inc. — Account No. 3

Date 19XX		Description	Post. Ref.	Debit	Credit	Balance

Name ______________________

Section ______________________

6-26A
Reed Wholesalers

(c)
[(c) is also in foldout section]

Sales Journal

Page 1

Date 19XX		Invoice No.	Account	Post. Ref.	Amount	

General Journal

Page 1

Date 19XX		Description	Post. Ref.	Debit	Credit

Name ______________________

Section ______________________

6-26A

Reed Wholesalers

(c) (continued)

Invoice Register

Page 1

Date 19XX	Account Credited	Post. Ref.	Accounts Payable Credit	Purchases Debit	Office Supplies on Hand Debit	Store Supplies on Hand Debit	Other Debits		
							Account	Post. Ref.	Amount

Name ____________________

Section ____________________

6-26A

Reed Wholesalers

(c) (continued)

Cash Disbursements Journal

Page 1

Date 19XX	Check No.	Description	Cash Credit	Purchases Discounts Credit	Accounts Payable		Other Accounts			
					Post. Ref.	Debit	Account	Post. Ref.	Debit	Credit

Name ______________________

Section ______________________

6-26A
Reed Wholesalers

Reed Wholesalers
Trial Balance
January 31, 19XX

(e)

				Debit	Credit

Name ______________________

Section ______________________

6-26A

Reed Wholesalers

Reed Wholesalers
Schedule of Accounts Receivable
(f)
January 31, 19XX

Reed Wholesalers
Schedule of Accounts Payable
January 31, 19XX

Name ______________________

Section ______________________

6-28A

Lambert, Inc.

[6–27A is in foldout section]

(a) and (b)

[(b) is also in foldout section and on p. 306]

General Ledger

Cash in Bank

Account No. 11

Date 19XX		Description	Post. Ref.	Debit*	Credit	Balance

Office Supplies on Hand

Account No. 17

Date 19XX		Description	Post. Ref.	Debit*	Credit	Balance

Equipment

Account No. 18

Date 19XX		Description	Post. Ref.	Debit*	Credit	Balance

Vouchers Payable

Account No. 21

Date 19XX		Description	Post. Ref.	Debit	Credit*	Balance

Name ______________________

Section ______________________

6-28A

Lambert, Inc.

General Ledger

(a) and (b) (*continued*)

Purchases

Account No. 51

Date 19XX		Description	Post. Ref.	Debit*	Credit	Balance

Purchases Returns and Allowances

Account No. 52

Date 19XX		Description	Post. Ref.	Debit	Credit*	Balance

Purchases Discounts

Account No. 53

Date 19XX		Description	Post. Ref.	Debit	Credit*	Balance

Transportation In

Account No. 54

Date 19XX		Description	Post. Ref.	Debit*	Credit	Balance

Name ____________________

Section ____________________

6-28A

Lambert, Inc.

General Ledger

(a) and (b) (*continued*)

Rent Expense — **Account No. 61**

Date 19XX		Description	Post. Ref.	Debit*	Credit	Balance

Utilities Expense — **Account No. 62**

Date 19XX		Description	Post. Ref.	Debit*	Credit	Balance

(c)

Lambert, Inc.
Schedule of Unpaid Vouchers
Jan. 31, 19XX

		Voucher No.	Name		Amount	

Name ______________________________

Section ______________________________

6-28A

Lambert, Inc.

(b) (continued)

Lambert, Inc.
Check Register

Page 1

Check No.	Date	Payee	Voucher No.	Vouchers Payable Debit	Purchases Discounts Credit	Cash in Bank Credit

Name ______________________

Section ______________________

6-29A

Decker Company

Decker Company
Check Register

[First part of 6–29A is in foldout section]

Page 1

Check No.	Date 19XX	Payee	Voucher No.	Vouchers Payable Debit	Purchases Discounts Credit	Cash in Bank Credit

Name ______________________

Section ______________________

(a) Sales Journal Columns:

(b) Invoice Register Columns:

(c) Cash Receipts Journal Columns:

(d) Cash Disbursements Journal Columns:

Name ______________________

Section ______________________

(a)

Balance Sheet
January 31, 1988

***Assets* (in thousands)**

Name ______________________

Section ______________________

(a) ***(continued)***

Liabilities and Stockholders' Equity **(in thousands)**
(b)

Name

Section

(a)

(b)

(c)

(d)

Name ____________________

Section ____________________

7-28

Wegner Distributors, Inc.

(a)

(b)

(c)

Name ____________________

Section ____________________

7-29

Various Companies

(a)

(b)

(c)

(d)

Name ______________________

Section ______________________

7-30
Murphy Company

Murphy Company
Bank Reconciliation
July 31, 19XX

(a)

Name ______________________

Section ______________________

7-30

Murphy Company

(b)

General Journal

Date 19XX		Description	Post. Ref.	Debit	Credit

Name ______________________

Section ______________________

7-31

Nanco, Inc.

(a)

Nanco, Inc.
Bank Reconciliation
September 30, 19XX

Name ______________________________

Section ______________________________

7-31

Nanco, Inc.

(b)

General Journal

Date 19XX		Description	Post. Ref.	Debit	Credit

Name ______________________________

Section ______________________________

7-32

Ruland, Inc.

General Journal

Date 19XX	Description	Post. Ref.	Debit	Credit

Name ____________________

Section ____________________

7-33

Rose Corporation

(a)

General Journal

Date 19X1		Description	Post. Ref.	Debit	Credit

Name ______________________

Section ______________________

7-33

Rose Corporation

(a) *(continued)*

General Journal

Date 19X1	*Description*	*Post. Ref.*	*Debit*	*Credit*

Name ______________________

Section ______________________

7-33

Rose Corporation

(b)

General Journal

Date 19X2	Description	Post. Ref.	Debit	Credit

Name ____________________

Section ____________________

7-34

Tysong Corporation

General Journal

Date 19X1		Description	Post. Ref.	Debit	Credit

Name ______________________

Section ______________________

7-34

Tysong Corporation

(continued)

General Journal

Date 19X1		Description	Post. Ref.	Debit	Credit

Name ______________________

Section ______________________

7-34

Tysong Corporation

(continued)

General Journal

Date 19X2		Description	Post. Ref.	Debit	Credit

Name ______________________

Section ______________________

7-28A
Arlington Company

Name ______________________

Section ______________________

7-29A

Twister

Name ______________________

Section ______________________

7-30A
Nahn Company

Nahn Company
Bank Reconciliation
May 31, 19XX

(a)

Name ______________________

Section ______________________

7-30A

Nahn Company

(b)

General Journal

Date 19XX		Description	Post. Ref.	Debit	Credit

Name ______________________

Section ______________________

7-31A

Monroe Company

Monroe Company
Bank Reconciliation
April 30, 19XX

(a)

Name ____________________

Section ____________________

7-31A

Monroe Company

(b)

General Journal

Date 19XX		Description	Post. Ref.	Debit	Credit

Name ____________________

Section ____________________

7-32A

Towell, Inc.

General Journal

Date 19XX		Description	Post. Ref.	Debit	Credit

Name ______________________

Section ______________________

7-33A

Madland Corporation

(a) **General Journal**

Date 19X1		Description	Post. Ref.	Debit	Credit

Name ____________________

Section ____________________

7-33A

Madland Corporation

(a) ***(continued)***

General Journal

Date 19X1		Description	Post. Ref.	Debit	Credit

Name ______________________

Section ______________________

7-33A

Madland Corporation

(a) ***(continued)*** **General Journal**

Date 19X2		Description	Post. Ref.	Debit	Credit
(b)					

Name ______________________

Section ______________________

7-34A

Yost Company

General Journal

Date 19X5		Description	Post. Ref.	Debit	Credit

Name ____________________

Section ____________________

7-34A

Yost Company

(continued)

General Journal

Date 19X5		Description	Post. Ref.	Debit	Credit

Name ____________________

Section ____________________

(a)

(b)

Name ______________________

Section ______________________

(continued)

(c)

(d)

Name ______________________

Section ______________________

8-25

Cahill, Inc.

(a)

(b)

(c)

Name ____________________

Section ____________________

8-26

Mason Company

(a) **General Journal** Page 1

Date 19XX		Description	Post. Ref.	Debit	Credit

Name ______________________

Section ______________________

8-26

Mason Company

(b)

Name ______________________

Section ______________________

8-27

Miller Company

(a)

(b)

Name ____________________

Section ____________________

8-28

Fairbanks Products, Inc.

(a)

General Journal

Date 19X1		Description	Post. Ref.	Debit	Credit

(b)

Name ____________________

Section ____________________

8-29

Post Company

(a) General Journal — Page 1

Date 19XX		Description	Post. Ref.	Debit	Credit

Name ______________________

Section ______________________

8-29

Post Company

(a) *(continued)*

General Journal

Page 2

Date 19XX		*Description*	*Post. Ref.*	*Debit*	*Credit*

(b)

General Journal

Page 3

Date 19XX		*Description*	*Post. Ref.*	*Debit*	*Credit*

Name ____________________

Section ____________________

8-30

Temple, Inc.

General Journal

Page 1

Date 19XX		Description	Post. Ref.	Debit	Credit

Name ______________________________

Section ______________________________

8-30

Temple, Inc.

(continued)

General Journal

Page 2

Date 19XX		*Description*	*Post. Ref.*	*Debit*	*Credit*

Name ____________________

Section ____________________

8-31

Sigma Corporation

(a) **General Journal** Page 1

Date 19X0		Description	Post. Ref.	Debit	Credit
(b)					
19X1					

Name ______________________

Section ______________________

8-31

Sigma Corporation

(c)

General Journal

Page 2

Date 19X1		Description	Post. Ref.	Debit	Credit

Name ______________________

Section ______________________

8-25A
Randwick, Inc.

(a)

(b)

(c)

Name ______________________

Section ______________________

8-26A

Spartan, Inc.

(a) **General Journal** Page 1

Date 19XX		Description	Post. Ref.	Debit	Credit

Name ______________________

Section ______________________

8-26A

Spartan, Inc.

(b)

Name ______________________

Section ______________________

8-27A

Pyramid Company

(a)

(b)

Name ______________________

Section ______________________

8-28A

Pioneer Corporation

(a) **General Journal** Page 1

Date 19X3		Description	Post. Ref.	Debit	Credit

Name ______________________

Section ______________________

8-28A

Pioneer Corporation

(b)

General Journal

Page 2

Date 19X4		Description	Post. Ref.	Debit	Credit

Name ______________________

Section ______________________

8-29A

Crescent Company

(a) **General Journal** Page 1

Date 19XX		Description	Post. Ref.	Debit	Credit

Name ____________________

Section ____________________

8-29A

Crescent Company

(a) *(continued)* **General Journal** Page 2

Date 19XX		*Description*	*Post. Ref.*	*Debit*	*Credit*

(b)

Name ______________________________

Section ______________________________

8-30A

Design, Inc.

General Journal

Page 1

Date 19XX		Description	Post. Ref.	Debit	Credit

Name ______________________

Section ______________________

8-30A

Design, Inc.

(continued)

General Journal

Page 2

Date 19XX	Description	Post. Ref.	Debit	Credit

Name ______________________

Section ______________________

8-30A
Design, Inc.

(continued) **General Journal** Page 3

Date 19XX		Description	Post. Ref.	Debit	Credit

Name ______________________

Section ______________________

8-31A

Centurion Corporation

(a)

General Journal

Page 1

Date 19X0	Description	Post. Ref.	Debit	Credit
(b)				

Name ______________________

Section ______________________

8-31A

Centurion Corporation

(c) **General Journal** Page 2

Date 19X1		Description	Post. Ref.	Debit	Credit

Name ____________________

Section ____________________

Ridgewood Sales, Inc.
Projected Income Statement

Name ______________________

Section ______________________

9-29

Grover Sales, Inc.

(a)

Name ______________________

Section ______________________

9-29

Grover Sales, Inc.

(a) ***(continued)***

(b)

(c)

Name ______________________

Section ______________________

9-29

Grover Sales, Inc.

(c) (*continued*)

Name ____________________

Section ____________________

9-30

Reed, Inc.

(a)

(b)

Name ______________________

Section ______________________

9-30

Reed, Inc.

(c)

(d)

Name ______________________

Section ______________________

9-30

Reed, Inc.

(d) (*continued*)

Name ______________________

Section ______________________

9-31

Suhey Company

(a)

(b)

(c)

(d)

(e)

Name ______________________

Section ______________________

9-32

Agase Company

(a)

(b)

Name ______________________

Section ______________________

9-33

Rochelle Company

(a)

(b)

Name ______________________

Section ______________________

9-34
Chipper Company

Name

Section

9-35

Haslem Company

(a) (1)

General Journal

Date	Description	Post. Ref.	Debit	Credit
	Periodic Inventory System			
(b)				

Name ____________________

Section ____________________

9-35

Haslem Company

(a) (2)

General Journal

Date		Description	Post. Ref.	Debit	Credit
		Perpetual Inventory System			
(b)					
(c)					

Name ____________________

Section ____________________

9-36

Breen Company

Inventory Control

(a)

Date	Received Units	Received Cost per Unit	Received Total	Sold Units	Sold Cost per Unit	Sold Total	Balance Units	Balance Cost per Unit	Balance Total

(b)

(c)

Name ____________________

Section ____________________

9-29A

Singer Sales, Inc.

(a)

Name ______________________

Section ______________________

9-29A

Singer Sales, Inc.

(a) (*continued*)

(b)

(c)

Name ______________________

Section ______________________

(c) ***(continued)***

Name ______________________

Section ______________________

9-30A

Winston, Inc.

(a)

(b)

Name ____________________

Section ____________________

9-30A

Winston, Inc.

(c)

(d)

Name ______________________

Section ______________________

9-30A

Winston, Inc.

(d) ***(continued)***

Name ____________________

Section ____________________

9-31A

Compact, Inc.

(a)

(b)

Name ____________________

Section ____________________

9-31A

Compact, Inc.

(c)

(d)

(e)

(f)

(g)

Name ______________________

Section ______________________

9-32A
Appling Company

(a)

Item	Quantity	Unit Price Cost	Unit Price Market
Desks			
Model 9001	80	$200	$205
Model 9002	45	300	282
Model 9003	20	375	385
Total—desks			
Cabinets			
Model 7001	170	60	65
Model 7002	80	90	88
Model 7003	40	120	124
Total—cabinets			

(b)

Name ____________________

Section ____________________

9-33A

Bock Company

(a)

(b)

Name

Section

9-34A

Ladd Company

(a)

(b)

Name ____________________

Section ____________________

9-35A

Corner Appliance Shop

(a) (1)

General Journal

Date		Description	Post. Ref.	Debit	Credit
		Periodic Inventory System			
(b)					

Name ______________________

Section ______________________

9-35A

Corner Appliance Shop

(a) (2)

General Journal

Date		Description	Post. Ref.	Debit	Credit
		Perpetual Inventory System			
(b)					
(c)					

Name ______________________

Section ______________________

9-36A
Merritt Company

Inventory Control

(a)

	Received			Sold			Balance		
		Cost			Cost			Cost	
		per			per			per	
Date	Units	Unit	Total	Units	Unit	Total	Units	Unit	Total

(b)

(c)

Name ______________________

Section ______________________

Chapter 9
Business Decision Problem
Redstone Company

Name ____________________

Section ____________________

10-29
Chavay Company

Expenditures and Receipts	Land	Building	Land Improvements

Name ______________________

Section ______________________

10-30

Beam Company

(a)

(b)

Date 19X3		Description	Post. Ref.	Debit	Credit

Name ____________________

Section ____________________

10-30

Beam Company

(c)

General Journal

Date 19X3		Description	Post. Ref.	Debit	Credit

Name ____________________

Section ____________________

10-31

Winkler, Inc.

(a)

(b)

(c)

(d)

Name ______________________

Section ______________________

10-32
Cyrus Company

(a)

General Journal

Date 19X5		Description	Post. Ref.	Debit	Credit

Name ______________________

Section ______________________

10-32
Cyrus Company

(b)

General Journal

Date 19X5		Description	Post. Ref.	Debit	Credit

Name ______________________

Section ______________________

10-33

Morgan Corporation

General Journal

Date 19X1		Description	Post. Ref.	Debit	Credit
19X2					

Name ______________________

Section ______________________

10-33

Morgan Corporation

(continued)

General Journal

Date 19X2	Description	Post. Ref.	Debit	Credit
19X3				

Name ______________________

Section ______________________

10-34

Valley Company

(a)

General Journal

Date 19X1		Description	Post. Ref.	Debit	Credit
19X2					
19X3					
19X4					

Name ______________________

Section ______________________

10-34

Valley Company

(a) (continued)

General Journal

Date 19X4		Description	Post. Ref.	Debit	Credit
(b)					

Name ______________________

Section ______________________

10-35

Kirle, Inc.

(a)

Name ______________________________

Section ______________________________

10-35
Kirle, Inc.

(b)

General Journal

Date 19X2		Description	Post. Ref.	Debit	Credit

Name ______________________________

Section ______________________________

10-29A

Sweeney Investment Company

Expenditures and Receipts	Land	Building	Land Improvements

Name ______________________

Section ______________________

10-30A
Berg Company

(a)

(b)

Date 19X4		Description	Post. Ref.	Debit	Credit

Name ____________________

Section ____________________

10-30A

Berg Company

(c)

General Journal

Date 19X4		Description	Post. Ref.	Debit	Credit

Name ______________________

Section ______________________

10-31A

Gooden Company

(a)

Name

Section

10-31A

Gooden Company

(b)

Name ____________________

Section ____________________

10-32A

Walcott Company

(a) **General Journal**

Date 19X6		Description	Post. Ref.	Debit	Credit

Name ____________________

Section ____________________

10-32A

Walcott Company

(b)

General Journal

Date 19X6		Description	Post. Ref.	Debit	Credit

Name ______________________________

Section ______________________________

10-33A

Quick Delivery Service

General Journal

Date 19X3		Description	Post. Ref.	Debit	Credit
19X4					

Name ______________________

Section ______________________

10-33A

Quick Delivery Service

(continued)

General Journal

Date 19X5		Description	Post. Ref.	Debit	Credit
19X6					

Name ______________________________

Section ______________________________

10-34A

Hirsch Company

(a)

General Journal

Date 19X1		Description	Post. Ref.	Debit	Credit
19X6					
19X7					

Name ______________________________

Section ______________________________

10-34A
Hirsch Company

(a) *(continued)*

General Journal

Date 19X7		Description	Post. Ref.	Debit	Credit
(b)					

Name ______________________

Section ______________________

10-35A
Image Company

(a)

Name

Section

10-35A
Image Company

(b)

General Journal

Date 19X1		Description	Post. Ref.	Debit	Credit

Name ______________________

Section ______________________

Chapter 10

Business Decision Problem

Waver, Inc.

Name ______________________

Section ______________________

11-29

Cardex Company

General Journal

Date		Description	Post. Ref.	Debit	Credit

Name ____________________

Section ____________________

11-29

Cardex Company

General Journal

Date		Description	Post. Ref.	Debit	Credit

Name ______________________

Section ______________________

11-30

Muir Construction Company

General Journal

Date 19X6		Description	Post. Ref.	Debit	Credit

Name ______________________________

Section ______________________________

11-31

Pike Gravel, Inc.

Name ____________________

Section ____________________

11-31

Pike Gravel, Inc.

Name ______________________

Section ______________________

11-32

Bluff Company

(a)

General Journal

Date 19X1	Description	Post. Ref.	Debit	Credit

Name ______________________________

Section ______________________________

11-32
Bluff Company

(b) *(continued)* **General Journal**

Date 19X1	*Description*	*Post. Ref.*	*Debit*	*Credit*

Name ______________________________

Section ______________________________

11-33
Kramer Company

(a) **General Journal**

Date 19X6		Description	Post. Ref.	Debit	Credit

Name ____________________

Section ____________________

11-33

Kramer Company

(a) (*continued*)

General Journal

Date 19X6		Description	Post. Ref.	Debit	Credit

Name ______________________

Section ______________________

11-34

Block Company

Block Company
Balance Sheet
December 31, 19X4

Assets			

Name ______________________

Section ______________________

11-34
Block Company

Block Company
Balance Sheet
December 31, 19X4

(continued)

Liabilities and Owner's Equity			

Name ______________________________

Section ______________________________

11-29A

Pollard Company

General Journal

Date		Description	Post. Ref.	Debit	Credit

Name ____________________

Section ____________________

11-29A

Pollard Company

General Journal

Date		Description	Post. Ref.	Debit	Credit

Name ____________________

Section ____________________

11-30A

Olin Excavators, Inc.

General Journal

Date 19X6		Description	Post. Ref.	Debit	Credit

Name ____________________

Section ____________________

11-31A

Pleasant Mining Company

Name ______________________

Section ______________________

11-31A

Pleasant Mining Company

Name ____________________

Section ____________________

11-32A

Steck Company

(a)

General Journal

Date 19X2		Description	Post. Ref.	Debit	Credit

Name ______________________

Section ______________________

11-32A

Steck Company

(b)

General Journal

Date 19X2		Description	Post. Ref.	Debit	Credit

Name ______________________

Section ______________________

11-33A

Worldly Publishers, Inc.

(a)

General Journal

Date 19X4		Description	Post. Ref.	Debit	Credit

Name ______________________________

Section ______________________________

11-33A

Worldly Publishers, Inc.

(b)

General Journal

Date 19X4		Description	Post. Ref.	Debit	Credit

Name ______________________

Section ______________________

Breen Company
Balance Sheet
December 31, 19X5

Assets			

Name ______________________________

Section ______________________________

11-34A
Breen Company

Breen Company
Balance Sheet
December 31, 19X5

(continued)

Liabilities and Owner's Equity			

Name ____________________

Section ____________________

Chapter 11
Business Decision Problem
Marin Company

Name ______________________

Section ______________________

12-24

Parker Company

Name ______________________

Section ______________________

12-25

Holland Corporation

(a)

(b)

Name ______________________

Section ______________________

12-26
Danville Corporation

(a)

General Journal

Date 19X1		Description	Post. Ref.	Debit	Credit
March	31				
(b)	31				
(c)	31				
(d)	31				

Name ______________________

Section ______________________

12-27

Summers Wholesale Company

(a)

General Journal

Date 19X5		Description	Post. Ref.	Debit	Credit
May	31				
(b)	31				
(c)	31				
(d)	31				

Name ______________________

Section ______________________

12-28

Racine Company

(a)

	Earnings			Deductions				
Employee	Regular	Over-time	Gross	FICA Tax	Federal Income Tax	Medical Insurance	Total	Net Earnings

Name

Section

12-28
Racine Company

(b) **General Journal** Page 1

Date 19XX		Description	Post. Ref.	Debit	Credit
Mar.	31	(1)			
	31	(2)			
	31	(3)			
(c)	31				
(d)	31				

Name ______________________

Section ______________________

12-28

Racine Company

(e) **General Journal** Page 2

Date 19XX		Description	Post. Ref.	Debit	Credit
Mar.	31				
(f)	31				

Name

Section

12-24A

Denton Company

Name ____________________

Section ____________________

12-25A

Carlton Corporation

(a)

(b)

Name ______________________

Section ______________________

12-26A

Gannon, Inc.

(a)

General Journal

Date 19X8		Description	Post. Ref.	Debit	Credit
Mar.	31				
(b)	31				
(c)	31				
(d)	31				

Name ______________________________

Section ______________________________

12-27A

Morrow Plumbing Company

(a)

General Journal

Date 19X4		Description	Post. Ref.	Debit	Credit
Mar.	31				
(b)	31				
(c)	31				
(d)	31				

Name ______________________

Section ______________________

12-28A

Bradford Company

(a)

	Earnings			Deductions				
Employee	Regular	Over-time	Gross	FICA Tax	Federal Income Tax	Medical Insurance	Total	Net Earnings

Name ______________________

Section ______________________

12-28A
Bradford Company

(b)

General Journal

Page 1

Date 19XX		Description	Post. Ref.	Debit	Credit
Mar.	31	(1)			
	31	(2)			
	31	(3)			
(c)	31				
(d)	31				

Name ______________________

Section ______________________

12-28A

Bradford Company

(e)

General Journal

Page 2

Date 19XX		Description	Post. Ref.	Debit	Credit
Mar.	31				
(f)	31				

Name

Section

Name ______________________

Section ______________________

13-28

Various Companies

(a)

(b)

Name ______________________

Section ______________________

13-29

Browning Realty Company

(a)

(b)

(c)

Name ______________________

Section ______________________

13-30

Unicom, Inc.

(a)

(b)

(c)

Name ______________________

Section ______________________

13-31

Companies A and B

(a)

(b)

(c)

(d)

(e)

Name

Section

13-32

Sage Company

(a)

(b)

(c)

(d)

Name ______________________

Section ______________________

13-33

Hofstad Corporation

(a)

(b)

(c)

(d)

Name ______________________

Section ______________________

13-28A

Various Companies

(a)

(b)

Name

Section

13-29A

Shelby Company

(a)

(b)

(c)

Name ______________________

Section ______________________

13-30A

Vessels, Inc.

(a)

(b)

(c)

Name ____________________

Section ____________________

13-31A

Companies C and D

(a)

(b)

(c)

(d)

(e)

Name ______________________

Section ______________________

13-32A
Roth Company

(a)

(b)

(c)

(d)

Name ______________________

Section ______________________

13-33A

Fryar Corporation

(a)

(b)

(c)

(d)

Name ____________________

Section ____________________

Name ______________________

Section ______________________

Name ______________________

Section ______________________

Name

Section

Name ______________________

Section ______________________

14-26

Grove and Fraser

(a) **General Journal** Page 1

Date 19XX		Description	Post. Ref.	Debit	Credit
(b)					

Name ______________________

Section ______________________

14-26

Grove and Fraser

(b) ***(continued)*** **General Journal** Page 2

Date 19XX		Description	Post. Ref.	Debit	Credit

Name

Section

14-27

Hayes, Kean, and Ladd

(a)

Name ____________________

Section ____________________

14-27

Hayes, Kean, and Ladd

(a) ***(continued)***

Name ______________________

Section ______________________

(b)

Name ______________________________

Section ______________________________

14-28

Bower, Daly, and Mack

(a) General Journal Page 1

Date 19XX		Description	Post. Ref.	Debit	Credit

Name ______________________________

Section ______________________________

14-29

Hope, Lucas, and Reece

(a) General Journal Page 1

Date	Description	Post. Ref.	Debit	Credit

Name ______________________

Section ______________________

14-30

Bolt, Drew, and Kiley

(a) **General Journal** Page 1

Date 19X1	Description	Post. Ref.	Debit	Credit

Name ____________________

Section ____________________

14-30

Bolt, Drew, and Kiley

(e)

General Journal

Page 2

Date		Description	Post. Ref.	Debit	Credit
(f)					

Name ______________________________

Section ______________________________

14-31

Judd, Karl, and Moran

Judd, Karl, and Moran
Statement of Partners' Capital
For the Year Ended December 31, 19X2

	Judd	Karl	Moran	Total

Name ______________________

Section ______________________

14-32

Carr, Hawk, and Lund

(a)
[(c) is in foldout section]

General Journal

Page 1

Date 19XX		Description	Post. Ref.	Debit	Credit

Name ____________________

Section ____________________

14-32

Carr, Hawk, and Lund

(b) **General Journal** Page 2

Date 19XX		Description	Post. Ref.	Debit	Credit

Name ______________________

Section ______________________

14-33

Abner, Boyd, Case, and Dunn

(a)

[(b) is in foldout section]

Name ______________________

Section ______________________

14-26A

Arden and Bolton

(a)

General Journal

Page 1

Date 19XX		Description	Post. Ref.	Debit	Credit

(b)

Name ______________________

Section ______________________

14-26A
Arden and Bolton

(b) ***(continued)*** **General Journal** Page 2

Date 19XX		Description	Post. Ref.	Debit	Credit

Name ______________________

Section ______________________

14-27A

Dean, Hagen, and Owen

(a)

Name ______________________

Section ______________________

14-27A

Dean, Hagen, and Owen

(a) ***(continued)***

Name ______________________

Section ______________________

14-27A

Dean, Hagen, and Owen

(b)

Name ______________________

Section ______________________

14-28A

Ford, Gibson, and Hanley

(a) General Journal Page 1

Date 19XX		Description	Post. Ref.	Debit	Credit

Name ______________________

Section ______________________

14-29A

Baker, Egan, and Lynn

(a)

General Journal

Page 1

Date 19XX		Description	Post. Ref.	Debit	Credit

Name ______________________________

Section ______________________________

14-30A

Casey, Kohl, and Mackey

(a) **General Journal** Page 1

Date 19X1		Description	Post. Ref.	Debit	Credit
(b)					

Name ______________________

Section ______________________

14-30A

Casey, Kohl, and Mackey

General Journal

Page 2

Date		Description	Post. Ref.	Debit	Credit

Name ______________________

Section ______________________

14-31A

Lucas, Brown, and Carter

Lucas, Brown, and Carter
Statement of Partners' Capital
For the Year Ended December 31, 19X2

	Lucas	Brown	Carter	Total

Name ______________________

Section ______________________

14-32A

Cody, Lyon, and Parker

(a)

[(c) is in foldout section]

General Journal

Page 1

Date 19XX		Description	Post. Ref.	Debit	Credit
(b)					

Name ______________________

Section ______________________

14-32A

Cody, Lyon, and Parker

(b) ***(continued)*** **General Journal** Page 2

Date 19XX		Description	Post. Ref.	Debit	Credit

Name ____________________

Section ____________________

14-33A

Beard, Dale, Gregg, and Ritt

(a)

[(b) is in foldout section]

Name ______________________

Section ______________________

Name ______________________

Section ______________________

15-28

Oaktree Corporation

(a)

General Journal

Date 19XX		Description	Post. Ref.	Debit	Credit

Name ____________________

Section ____________________

15-28
Oaktree Corporation

(b)

Name ______________________________

Section ______________________________

15-29

Plano Corporation

	Dividend Distribution		
	Preferred	Common	Total
(a)			
(b)			
(c)			

Name ______________________

Section ______________________

15-29

Plano Corporation

Dividend Distribution

	Preferred	Common	Total
(d)			

Name ______________________

Section ______________________

15-30
Ingram Corporation

(a) and (b)

6% Preferred Stock

	Bal.	120,000

Paid-in Capital in Excess of Par Value—Preferred Stock

	Bal.	96,000

Common Stock

	Bal.	500,000

Retained Earnings

	Bal.	270,000

Name ______________________________

Section ______________________________

15-30

Ingram Corporation

(b) **General Journal** Page 1

Date 19XX		Description	Post. Ref.	Debit	Credit

Name ______________________________

Section ______________________________

15-30
Ingram Corporation

(b) ***(continued)*** **General Journal** Page 2

Date 19XX	Description	Post. Ref.	Debit	Credit
(c)				

Name ____________________

Section ____________________

15-30

Ingram Corporation

(d)

Name ______________________________

Section ______________________________

15-31

Whistler, Inc.

General Journal

Date 19X2		Description	Post. Ref.	Debit	Credit

Name ______________________

Section ______________________

15-31

Whistler, Inc.

(continued)

General Journal

Date 19X2		Description	Post. Ref.	Debit	Credit

Name ______________________

Section ______________________

15-32

Sabin Corporation

(a)

(b)

(c)

Name ____________________

Section ____________________

15-33
Macklin Corporation

(a) and (b)

7% Preferred Stock

	Bal. 400,000

Paid-in Capital in Excess of Par Value—Preferred Stock

	Bal. 12,000

Common Stock

	Bal. 600,000

Paid-in Capital in Excess of Par Value—Common Stock

	Bal. 480,000

Retained Earnings

	Bal. 325,000

Name ______________________

Section ______________________

15-33

Macklin Corporation

(b) General Journal Page 1

Date 19XX		Description	Post. Ref.	Debit	Credit

Name ____________________

Section ____________________

15-33

Macklin Corporation

(b) ***(continued)***

General Journal

Page 2

Date 19XX		Description	Post. Ref.	Debit	Credit

Name ______________________
Section ______________________

15-33
Macklin Corporation

(c)

Name ______________________________

Section ______________________________

15-28A

Dylan Corporation

(a) **General Journal**

Date 19XX	Description	Post. Ref.	Debit	Credit

Name ______________________

Section ______________________

15-28A

Dylan Corporation

(b)

Name ______________________

Section ______________________

15-29A

Busch Corporation

	Dividend Distribution		
	Preferred	Common	Total
(a)			
(b)			
(c)			

Name ______________________

Section ______________________

15-29A
Busch Corporation

	Dividend Distribution		
	Preferred	Common	Total
(d)			

Name ______________________

Section ______________________

15-30A

Stork Corporation

(a) and (b)

	Bal. 800,000

	Bal. 580,000

	Bal. 353,000

Name ____________________

Section ____________________

15-30A

Stork Corporation

(b)

General Journal

Page 1

Date 19XX		Description	Post. Ref.	Debit	Credit

Name ______________________________

Section ______________________________

15-30A
Stork Corporation

(b) ***(continued)*** **General Journal** Page 2

Date 19XX		Description	Post. Ref.	Debit	Credit
(c)					
(d)					

Name ______________________

Section ______________________

15-31A

Dawkins, Inc.

General Journal

Page 1

Date 19XX		Description	Post. Ref.	Debit	Credit

Name ______________________

Section ______________________

15-31A

Dawkins, Inc.

(continued)

General Journal

Page 2

Date 19XX		Description	Post. Ref.	Debit	Credit

Name

Section

15-32A

Mannheim, Inc.

(a)

(b)

(c)

Name

Section

15-33A
Cloud Corporation

(a) and (b)

8% Preferred Stock

	Bal. 200,000

Paid-in Capital in Excess of Par Value—Preferred Stock

	Bal. 28,000

Common Stock

	Bal. 750,000

Paid-in Capital in Excess of Par Value—Common Stock

	Bal. 250,000

Retained Earnings

	Bal. 290,000

Name ____________________

Section ____________________

15-33A

Cloud Corporation

(b) **General Journal** Page 1

Date 19XX	Description	Post. Ref.	Debit	Credit

Name ______________________

Section ______________________

15-33A
Cloud Corporation

(b) ***(continued)*** **General Journal** Page 2

Date 19XX		Description	Post. Ref.	Debit	Credit

Name ______________________

Section ______________________

15-33A
Cloud Corporation

(c)

Name ____________________

Section ____________________

Chapter 15
Business Decision Problem
Hardware City, Inc.

(a) ***(continued)***
[(a) begins in foldout section]

General Journal

Page 1

Date 19XX		Description	Post. Ref.	Debit	Credit

(a) *(continued)* **General Journal** Page 2

Date 19XX		Description	Post. Ref.	Debit	Credit

Name ______________________________

Section ______________________________

Hardware City, Inc.
Balance Sheet
June 1, 19XX

(a) ***(continued)***

Name

Section

(b)

(c)

Name ______________________________

Section ______________________________

16-29

Checker Corporation

(a)

General Journal

Date 19X2		Description	Post. Ref.	Debit	Credit

Name ______________________________

Section ______________________________

16-29

Checker Corporation

(b)

Checker Corporation
Retained Earnings Statement
For the Year Ended December 31, 19X2

Name ______________________________

Section ______________________________

16-29
Checker Corporation

(c)

General Journal

Date 19X3	Description	Post. Ref.	Debit	Credit
(d)				

Name ____________________

Section ____________________

16-30
Basin Corporation

(a) **General Journal**

Date 19X4		Description	Post. Ref.	Debit	Credit

Name ______________________

Section ______________________

16-30

Basin Corporation

Basin Corporation
Retained Earnings Statement
For the Year Ended December 31, 19X4

(b)

Name ______________________

Section ______________________

16-31

Mauer Corporation

(a)

General Journal

Page 1

Date 19X2		Description	Post. Ref.	Debit	Credit

Name ______________________

Section ______________________

16-31

Mauer Corporation

(a) (continued)

General Journal

Page 2

Date 19X2		*Description*	*Post. Ref.*	*Debit*	*Credit*

Name ______________________

Section ______________________

16-31

Mauer Corporation

Mauer Corporation
Retained Earnings Statement
For the Year Ended December 31, 19X2

(b)

Name ____________________

Section ____________________

16-31

Mauer Corporation

(c)

Stockholders' Equity

Name ______________________________

Section ______________________________

16-32

Munn Corporation

(a) **General Journal**

Date 19X2		Description	Post. Ref.	Debit	Credit

Name ____________________

Section ____________________

16-32

Munn Corporation

(b)

Munn Corporation
Statement of Stockholders' Equity
For the Year Ended December 31, 19X2

Name ______________________________

Section ______________________________

16-33

Sycamore Company

Sycamore Company
Income Statement
For the Year Ended December 31, 19X1

(a)

Name ______________________

Section ______________________

(b)

Sycamore Company
Income Statement
For the Year Ended December 31, 19X1

Name ______________________

Section ______________________

16-34

Genoa Corporation

Name ______________________

Section ______________________

16-35

Faircrest Corporation

Faircrest Corporation
Income Statement
For the Year Ended December 31, 19X3

Name ______________________

Section ______________________

16-29A

Penn Corporation

(a) **General Journal**

Date 19X8		Description	Post. Ref.	Debit	Credit

Name ______________________

Section ______________________

16-29A

Penn Corporation

(b)

Penn Corporation
Retained Earnings Statement
For the Year Ended December 31, 19X8

Name ______________________________

Section ______________________________

16-29A
Penn Corporation

(c)

General Journal

Date 19X9	Description	Post. Ref.	Debit	Credit

Name ______________________

Section ______________________

16-30A

Avenue Corporation

(a)

General Journal

Date 19X5		Description	Post. Ref.	Debit	Credit

Name

Section

16-30A

Avenue Corporation

(b)

Avenue Corporation
Retained Earnings Statement
For the Year Ended December 31, 19X5

Name ____________________

Section ____________________

16-31A

Dover Corporation

(a)

General Journal

Page 1

Date 19X4		Description	Post. Ref.	Debit	Credit

Name ______________________________

Section ______________________________

16-31A

Dover Corporation

(a) ***(continued)*** **General Journal** Page 2

Date 19X4		Description	Post. Ref.	Debit	Credit

Name ____________________

Section ____________________

16-31A

Dover Corporation

Dover Corporation
Retained Earnings Statement
For the Year Ended December 31, 19X4

(b)

Name ______________________

Section ______________________

16-31A
Dover Corporation

(c)

		Stockholders' Equity		

Name ____________________

Section ____________________

16-32A

Savard Company

Name ______________________

Section ______________________

16-33A

Galley Company

Galley Company
Income Statement
For the Year Ended December 31, 19X3

(a)

Name ______________________________

Section ______________________________

16-33A

Galley Corporation

Galley Corporation
Retained Earnings Statement
For the Year Ended December 31, 19X3

(b)

Name ______________________

Section ______________________

16-34A

Midland Corporation

Name ______________________________

Section ______________________________

16-35A

Hilltop Corporation

Hilltop Corporation
Income Statement
For the Year Ended December 31, 19X2

Name ______________________

Section ______________________

Name

Section